Multiple Mini Interviews for Medical School

Southampton:
+44 2380594408

ugapply.sm@southampton.ac.uk

Dawn Sellars

Multiple Mini Interviews for Medical School

Spine Publishing, Dr Prep Ltd, CPC1, Capital Park, Fulbourn, Cambridge, CB21 5XE

© Dawn Sellars 2012

All rights reserved. No part of this publication may be reproduced, stored in a retrieval system or transmitted in any form or by any means, electronic and mechanical, photocopying, recording or otherwise without prior permission of the publisher.

British Library Cataloguing in Publication Data

A catalogue record for this book is available from the British Library

ISBN 0-9551325-8-4 / 978-0-9551325-8-2

Contents

**GAMSAT, UKCAT, BMAT,
Personal Statement & Interview
Preparation**

***Our courses, held in London, comprise
Lectures, Handouts, Mock Exam, Extra
Practice Questions & Feedback.
Correspondence courses also available.***

mail@drprep.com

07747634081

www.drprep.net

Contributors

Juliet Booth BA (Hons)

Rose Brennan

Benjamin Carey MA (Oxon)

Ben Fenner

Katherine Green MBChB

Anna May Mangan

Kate McCombe MBBS, MRCP, FRCA

Madeline Payne

Phyllida Roe BA (Hons), BSc (Hons), BMBS, DHMSA

Dawn Sellars MA (Cantab), MBBS, MRCGP

Hannah Smoker BA (Hons)

The Editor

Dawn Sellars graduated from Cambridge University with a degree in Natural Sciences in 1997. She then worked in NHS management before returning to academia with the Institute of Cancer Research. She is now a GP, having achieved 99 in the GP Clinical Skills Assessment. She is also a trained OSCE examiner for a London Medical School as well as being the managing director of Dr Prep Ltd, a company which specialises in preparing candidates for entry into medical school. She is also the primary author of 'How to get into Graduate Entry Medicine'.

Introduction

Over the past few years, there have been many changes in medical school admissions, such as the introduction of exams such as MSAT (which came and went within a few years), GAMSAT and UKCAT, as well as different types of interview format.

In the past, medical school interviews have tended to assess candidates' personalities in a relatively unstructured way, and interviewers were invariably offered broad scope with their questions. At its extreme, interviews have been reported as an 'armchair chat' about sport, followed by an offer if the correct rugby team were supported. Union of course!

Whilst most interview styles will have resulted in the right people being selected, as evidenced by the marvellous doctors found within our NHS, there has been a shift towards greater transparency and objectivity, largely due to the suggestions contained within the white paper *'Tomorrow's Doctors'*. The shift has also been seen with the change in clinical examinations at medical schools from viva-style cases with a single senior clinician, to a series of objective structured clinical examinations (OSCEs) with a number of different examiners, thus reducing the potential for prejudice.

For the last decade or so, many schools have started to adopt highly 'structured' interviews. These are interviews with pre-prepared questions and limited, if any, scope for additional questions. This reducing the chance of bias due to too much rapport being established between interviewer and candidate, or conversely, a personality clash. Multiple Mini-Interviews, or MMIs, just like OSCEs, are a series of short assessments, often five minutes long. These can be thought of as a series of highly structured interviews. Rather than the series of questions being asked by one panel, the series of questions is asked by a series of interviewers, again further reducing the chance of bias and prejudice.

MMIs also lend themselves well to the inclusion of unusual tasks which assess some of the skills required of doctors. Other formats used to assess medical school applicants have included team work and written assessments. It all makes sense really. You know that medical schools are looking for communication skills, empathy, team work, realism, integrity, evidence of work experience, ability to handle stress, and so forth, so why not test each of these items in different stations, using specific tasks which best assess these criteria?

Two tasks previously used at St George's, the pioneers of all things new in medical school, have been widely discussed:

The first is a 'breaking bad news' station. The scenario was, in essence, that you were looking after the neighbour's pet, let it lose, resulting in its untimely demise under the wheels of a passing vehicle. You had to convey this to the neighbour (i.e.

the actor). This is interesting - breaking bad news is something that is taught, very well and at length, at medical school. In the same way that you won't know too much about ECGs at the moment, you will also have a lot to learn about breaking bad news. But you should be able to show potential in this regard, and so this type of scenario should indeed separate those candidates who can from those who shouldn't.

The other widely discussed task has been 'the shoe lace' station. In essence, candidates were asked to instruct the actor how to tie his shoe lace, without helping. A tricky thing to do, and when I first heard of this station I could imagine fretful instructions 'over, no under, no, the other one, over to your left, no, the other left....'. If you are asked to perform a task in an MMI which strikes you as bizarre, take a moment to think 'Why are they asking me to do this?' As a doctor, I have never had to explain to anyone how to tie their shoe laces, but I have had to explain many bizarre things to many bizarre people, often employing bizarre communication skills to achieve this aim. Hopefully I am reasonably good at it, and hopefully I would therefore have been OK at the shoe lace task, had that sort of thing been around in my day.

A note to the nervy: the actors employed by medical schools are usually professional actors. They take pride in their work and are good at getting into character. It would perhaps be reasonable to test a candidate's ability to handle an angry or sad individual for instance, so try not to be too thrown by how realistic the situation might be. And remember that whilst Julia Roberts won't be there, some of the actors may be recognisable. I remember one of my colleagues being quite thrown by the appearance of an old Grange Hill headmistress in one of her OSCE stations.

There has been some evidence to suggest that traditional interview formats do not accurately predict performance at medical school. At Dr Prep Ltd, we find this hard to fathom. At our courses, we see you perform in a group, an MMI, and a one-to-one interview, and we have met several hundred candidates. Those who are good tend to be good, period. We don't tend to see a candidate perform well at MMI and then go on to be a prize numpty in their one-to-one interview. My point is this: focus on the skills the schools are looking for and how these have been demonstrated during your work experience and leave the frills to the medical schools. As far as I'm concerned, it's all an elaborate variation on a theme, and those who deserve to get in tend to do so, and those who don't tend to be rejected. Of course there's the large number of people who are good enough but are beaten on the day, and you'll have to reapply whether it's a traditional interview, an MMI, or whatever new fangled thing they come up with next year.

Dawn Sellars
MA (Cantab) MBBS MRCGP
Managing Director Dr Prep Ltd

Medical Schools

Multiple mini interviews (MMI) are to be used during selection to seventeen medicine courses for 2013 entry. This chapter gives an overview of all of the medical schools' interview structures, followed by the experiences of many candidates who applied for 2012 entry, where possible. We have often been able to detail questions from more than one candidate, so there are far more questions listed than you would expect to be asked at a single interview! Of course, some schools will be using MMI for the first time, but we have included students accounts (from before the introduction of MMI) in case it gives you some insight into the 'culture' of the school. We would recommend that you read the information from other schools too, as all of the questions could be asked by any school!

In the chapters that follow we will take the various themes which recur in the schools questions, looking separately at, for instance, questions arising from personal statements, ethics questions, work experience and so forth.

Remember that this information is only correct at the time of going to press, and you must check the schools' latest information before your interview, and any other information upon which you are reliant.

Schools using MMI for selection in 2012 - 2013:

- Aberdeen
- Birmingham Standard Entry
- Birmingham Graduate Entry
- Dundee
- East Anglia
- Edinburgh Graduate Entry
- Keele
- King's Graduate Entry
- Lancaster
- Leeds
- Leicester Standard Entry
- Leicester Graduate Entry
- Manchester
- Nottingham Graduate Entry
- Queens Belfast

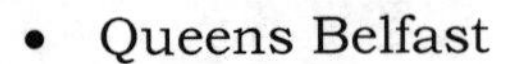

- St Georges Standard Entry
- St Georges Graduate Entry

Aberdeen A100 **From the university:**

MMIs : New for 2013 entry

The interview format at Aberdeen is to change from a 2-man panel who question in 3 domains to a Multiple Mini Interview (MMI) format:

- Each candidate will rotate round 5 separate questioning stations in turn
- Each station will last 7 minutes with one Selector scoring performance against criteria
- 2 minutes between stations
- Individual stations will cover one domain or questioning area
- Communication and interpersonal skills will also be scored at each station
- The areas we will be assessing over the 5 stations include
    - Commitment to medicine
    - Core qualities of a doctor
    - Teamwork and
    - Communication skills

Birmingham A100 and A101 **From the university:**

MMIs : New for 2013 entry. Applicants for the graduate-entry medicine programme will be interviewed on separate dates but will be expected to participate in the same stations.
There will be four separate, short interviews, lasting 6 minutes each. A range of your personal attributes relevant to studying medicine will be assessed by means of different tasks.

Interview stations are designed to assess aspects such as:

- motivation for medicine
- communication
- self-insight
- ethical reasoning
- scientific understanding and interpretation

The four stations will be:

- Data interpretation:
  You will be presented with the findings of a study and asked to interpret and discuss these.
- Motivation and insight into medicine:
  You will be asked to discuss specific aspects of your work experience.
- Dealing with personal and ethical challenges:
  Through thinking about your own experiences and an ethical problem, you have the opportunity to demonstrate personal qualities important for coping in a demanding career.

- Interactive task:
  This is a role-play station. You will be expected to achieve a task through negotiation with the role-player (who will be a medicine student).

Preparation for interview and indeed for study on a medicine programme is aided by engaging in frequent discussions with friends and family about medical issues appearing in the news and media. You should also use your time on work experience effectively by gaining insight into the demands placed on staff, the problems they encounter and the strategies that they employ to handle difficult situations as well as the benefits they obtain from caring for people and working in teams. Again, opportunities to engage in discussion of these issues must be taken.

Birmingham A100 **From the candidates:**

Remember that this is from last year's candidates, i.e. before MMI was used:

Short written exercise whilst waiting at the start. Apparently this did not count for anything but were considering using them as part of the process in future years. Mine was a short question with very basic physics. Mine was about how James Bond would be able to breathe using a reed underwater in order to survive .

It was a formal interview with two academic members of staff on the panel and a medical student observing. Questions included:

- Have you had any other medical interviews so far?

- Some questions about my personal statement, interests and hobbies.
- Why Birmingham?
- Why medicine?
- Also an ethical scenario about whether women should be paid for egg donation. No time was given to prepare but the story had been in the news in the preceding weeks.
- Tell us about a newspaper article you have read recently.
- Structure of a doctors' career post graduation.

It is crucial to keep up to date with recent news stories and researched how your career will progress

Birmingham A101 **From the candidates:**

Remember that this is from last year's candidates, i.e. before MMI was used:

Questions included:

- Why would a previous degree help to study medicine?
- Why Birmingham?
- Many questions arising from the personal statement.

Brighton and Sussex A100 From the university:

- A formal 20 minute semi-structured interview
- There are no set questions and the panel may refer to your personal statement and reference but also questions that may include your insights into NHS healthcare and areas such as ethics and professionalism within a healthcare setting.
- Each interviewer will score you out of 5. Depending on the calibre of the other interviewees; 13/15 allowed you an offer last year.

Brighton and Sussex A100 From the candidates:

Relatively formal, with 3 interviewers. Included:

- Why medicine?
- Work experience and other things I mentioned on my personal statement.
- Asked what the majority of the NHS health budget should be spent on.
- Also the importance of science in medicine and the difference between a doctor's and nurse's job.
- An ethical dilemma: If there is a shortage of donor organs, would you pass a law allowing for any healthy organs to be taken from those who have just passed away (but have not been able to give consent)? This was asked on the spot; there as no time to prepare.
- There were quite a few mature and/or graduate applicants there.

Bristol A100 & A101 — From the university:

The interviews last for 15 to 20 minutes, and are conducted by 2 interviewers, at least one of whom is a member of the Medical Admissions Committee.

Criteria for assessing the candidate's performance at interview:

- Reasons for wishing to study medicine
- Ability to communicate
- Self-confidence and enthusiasm
- Evidence of extramural activities
- Awareness of current developments
- Ability to develop coherent stance on a topical subject
- Informed about university and course
- Informed about career
- Overall impression created by candidate.

Each criterion is assessed on a six-point scale.

Bristol A101 — From the candidates:

The interview was only 15 minutes long, so few questions were asked, which included:

- Why medicine?
- Why Bristol?
- How do you cope with stress?
- What makes a good leader and good team member?
- Give examples of recent ethical issues that have been raised in the media.

Cambridge A100 & A101 **From the university:**

Dependent on college

Cambridge A100 **From the candidates:**

I had two interviews, one general with the admissions tutor and one scientific with two interviewers, the directors of the college's preclinical and clinical studies.
The general interview was more relaxed;

- Questions regarding my personal statement.
- Questions about recent medical news.
- Whether women should have the right to choose whether to have caesarean or not and why.
- I was asked if denying an elderly patient invasive heart surgery would be age discrimination.
- Lots of questions on my AS/2 level biology
- Scenario relating to how to deal with a mistake.

The scientific interview was more formal.
I was presented with graph axis and asked to draw three graphs of plasma drug concentration against time:

1. If the drug had been taken orally.
2. If taken by IV.
3. If taken by IV at half the rate of the original IV.

While doing this I had to explain the graph at each point and what was happening. I then had to talk about how a drug is removed from a body's system via the liver and kidneys. I was then asked how venous return works and how breathing helps this, I was asked to explain how a bell jar works to explain this analogy.

2 interviews each 15 minutes. First Interview:

- Why medicine?
- Why not biochemistry?
- How would you contribute to college life?
- Describe human genome project and implications for treatment. What are problems with it?
- Which diseases are caused by single gene disorders?
- Then a long discussion about the role of stomach in digestion, which was where I was pushed to my limits.

Second interview:

- There were a number of questions relating to my personal statement.
- Asked why not vet or nursing?
- How did you prepare for interview?
- Asked how I found BMAT and if I found it easy?
- Do you read? Tell about 3 medically related articles recently in newspapers.

Cambridge A101 **From the candidates:**

Panel interview, 4 interviewers,

- Questions on teamwork
- Questions on work experience
- Outside academic interests
- Why Cambridge? Why graduate medicine?
- The stresses of being a doctor
- Attributes of a good doctor

- Academic activity that has excited you?
- What lessons have you learnt about medicine?
- How doctors keep themselves up to date.

Science Question

- About a graph on heart rate/questions on equilibria.
- Given the concentration of ketamine and have to work out the amount that should be administed to the dog over a 5 hour time period. Needed to calculate dilution factor needed and to draw a graph showing the conc. of ketamine in the dog's body over the 5 hour period.

Also an ethical dilemma; given 10 minutes preparation;

- What would you do if a fellow doctor was lying
- The practical and ethical issues raised by an elderly person in a coma with little hope of surviving. What are the ethical and practical implications?
- Smokers and the NHS (are they deserving of treatment and lung transplants?)
- Obesity and the NHS (the affect it has on NHS and why obesity is rising in UK)
- Questions on consent and capacity.

There was little opportunity to talk about myself. I managed to create opportunities to talk about these things once or twice but they were very keen to push through with their questions. I felt it was a very one sided 'conversation'; more like an interrogation. I thought the whole thing went very badly, but I got an offer!

Cardiff A100 **From the university:**

The aim of the interview is to explore the non-academic criteria (below) and to encourage applicants to talk naturally about themselves, their studies and their experiences, and to demonstrate that they have the interpersonal skills to be able to communicate effectively and whether they have a balanced approach to life. In this way they can show how they meet the academic and non-academic attributes required of a prospective doctor. Interviews normally last 20 minutes. All applicants are expected to demonstrate evidence of:

- Motivation and interest in studying medicine
- Understanding the demands of medical training
- A caring ethos and sense of social awareness and responsibility
- Evidence of a balanced approach to life
- Interpersonal and communication skills.

Cardiff A100 **From the candidates:**

A very informal interview. Questions such as:

- Why medicine?
- Why Cardiff?
- A few questions about my personal statement.
- An ethical scenario of having an elderly neighbour whose property was falling into neglect and I was asked what action I would take.
- The medical student asked me how I would be involved in student life while I was at Cardiff.

University of Dundee A100 **From the university:**

The University of Dundee divides its medical school interview process into a series of 10 seven minute 'mini interviews', and has been using MMI since 2008 admission.

The usual topics are covered; you can expect to be asked about your understanding of: a medical career, the curriculum in Dundee, aspects of your UCAS statement as well as current medical issues in the press, including ethical topics.

In addition we will be looking to assess your communication skills and approach towards teamwork through a series of interactive stations where you have a task to complete or actor to talk to.

Durham (Newcastle) A100 From the university:

The purpose of the interview is to confirm whether the candidate has the aptitude, motivation and personal qualities to succeed as a medical student and as a potential doctor of the future. The interview will be conducted by 2 selectors and takes about 45 minutes.

We will be looking for your experience of interacting with people in a caring environment. We are particularly interested in recruiting local students, both school leavers and mature applicants, but applicants are welcomed equally from across the UK and EU.

Durham (Newcastle) A100 From the candidates:

The interview was 15 minutes long with 2 interviewers.
After some very standard initial questions, there was a clinical scenario. I had to pretend to be a GP who had been called out on a night visit to a man who needs to be admitted to the hospital for heart problems however the man is known to have psychological issues which may cause him distress and worsen his heart problem. The decision had to be made as to whether or not you should admit him. They then advised you that the decision you had made caused the man to deteriorate and they asked if you should have done anything differently.

University of East Anglia A100 From the university:

Each interview lasts approximately 50 minutes. Candidates will be invited to take part in an OSCE (Objective Structured Clinical Examination) style interview, also known as a Multiple Mini Interview, with academics and practicing clinicians. When candidates enter the interview section, they will find a series of booths, known as 'stations'. There will be seven stations to circulate through, spending approximately 5 minutes at each station. Further details will be provided to each candidate at the time they are invited to interview.

University of East Anglia A100 From the candidates:

MMI:

- Where have you seen an application of good communication skills? What have you learnt from this situation?
- What from your work experience has confirmed your desire to do medicine?
- Have you ever experienced a PBL style situation before?
- What is empathy? Describe an experience where you have seen someone acting without empathy
- What will you do if you don't get in this year?
- What are the four ethical principles of medicine? Where have you seen these being applied?
- Tell me about your personal statement
- Describe something you are proud off
- What act/occasion caused your interest in medicine?
- What do you think of the work of junior doctors?

- Standard question about leadership and team member roles.
- What do you know about PBL
- Asked about a difficult situation, its outcome, and what I could have done differently
- What is empathy and why is it an important skill for doctors
- What skills do you have that would make you a good doctor
- Scenario; you are on work experience and the doctor you are shadowing receives a page to say a patient is going into labour and asks if you want to join him. The patient speaks no English; what are the issues here.
- One interviewer seemed to be awkward on purpose and kept asking for more answers.
- How do you go about researching something?
- What difficulties do you think a mature student might face?
- Why should we choose you?
- Tell me about something you are proud of?
- Jehovah's Witness admitted with hypovolaemia what would you do?
- Man not fit for surgery due to smoking and obesity how would you explain this to him?

University of Edinburgh A100 **From the university:**

School leavers not normally interviewed.

Only short-listed graduate and mature applicants will be interviewed. Their MMI system was first used for 2008 entry.
The interview lasts for 35 minutes and is made up of three, ten minute sessions with two interviewers.
The areas covered are:

- Career exploration
- Ethics
- Communication skills

The ethics and communication skills questions will be provided on arrival at the interview and the applicant will be given 20 minutes in total to prepare for these questions.

University of Exeter A100 From the university:

Successful candidates at the initial application stage will be invited to an interview which is designed to determine whether applicants have the non-academic qualities such as the communication skills, reflectiveness and empathy required to become a successful doctor. Interviews will be conducted by a panel of interviewers, including at least one medical clinician. All interviews will be conducted on an individual basis, rather than conducted as a group, and while there is no specific preparation interviewees can undertake in preparation, time will be given prior to the interview to prepare for a series of scenario-based questions.
Exeter has no plans to use MMI.

University of Exeter A100 From the candidates:

See Peninsula

University of Glasgow A100 From the university:

The interview is structured and consists of two interviewers (e.g. School of Medicine staff, consultants and honorary members of the University) assessing:

- Why Medicine
- View of personal academic achievements
- Problem-solving abilities
- Understanding of medical careers
- Curricula and Glasgow curriculum
- Work experience
- Discussion of topical medical issue
- Evidence of team working, ability to get on with people

University of Glasgow A100 From the candidates:

The interview was 15 minutes long and was split into two halves. There were two interviewers and they took it in turns to either conduct the interview or write notes on the interview. The first half of the interview asked questions about our personal statement, including our work experience and subjects at school. The second half asked questions testing our knowledge of the course and in particular PBL and asked reasons for why we picked medicine and Glasgow in particular.
I think it would be worth mentioning that in this interview there was a type of good cop bad cop situation so interviewees should not be too worried if one half of the interview seems to go badly.

Hull York Medical School A100 From the university:

You will normally be interviewed by two people, typically one female and one male, one of whom is typically an experienced clinician. Your interviewers will not have seen your UCAS form, because the interview explores different attributes that are not well assessed from a written application.

Your interview will last about 20 minutes. It will be formally structured, with a fixed number of questions. One question will be based on an article that you will be given to read immediately beforehand. The article will be short and non-technical, of the type you might find in a broadsheet newspaper.

The other questions will explore the following attributes:

- knowledge and understanding of problem-based learning
- motivation for medicine
- depth and breadth of interests, knowledge and reflection about medicine and the wider world
- teamwork and work experience
- personal insight - knowledge of own strengths and weaknesses
- understanding of the role of medicine in society
- tolerance of uncertainty and ambiguity

The two interviewers will independently evaluate each answer and score your interview out of 50. Their two scores are averaged to give your interview score.

Imperial A100 **From the university:**

The interviewers will evaluate:

- Motivation and realistic approach to medicine as a career
- Capacity to deal with stressful situations
- Evidence of working as a leader and a team member
- Ability to multitask
- Likely contribution to university life
- Communication skills and maturity of character

Imperial A101 **From the university:**

In addition to the above, the interviewers will evaluate:

- Medical research as a career
- Understanding of mammalian cell biology
- To think logically and draw conclusions from data

Imperial A100 **From the candidates:**

4 panel members including one student, 15mins at most;

- What can you bring to the medical school?
- Why medicine? Why Imperial?
- Tell us about your work experience
- Personal statement, time management, team work etc.
- Asked about my extra-curricular activities
- What do you enjoy doing?
- What societies are you thinking of joining and your contribution to university life?
- What is your biggest fear with regard to medicine?
- Is hospital medicine or general practice more difficult?

- "If you were dictator, how would you tackle obesity?"
- Also "Should patients be able to request to see a doctor of the same ethnicity as themselves?"

One interviewer was kind, one was distant and the other kept his head down. The student seemed even more nervous than I did.

Imperial A101 **From the candidates:**

The panel consisted of 3 doctors who were all academic teachers and also a current medical student, they asked;

- Why medicine? Why Imperial?
- A number of academic questions
- Asked how I juggle lots of commitments at once?
- What can you bring to Imperial?
- What is your biggest fear with regard to medicine?
- 3 fairly easy science questions interpreting graphs.
- Asked about my GCSEs and if I have improved enough since then to take on the medical degree.

On one occasion I bought up my work experience and was told, "We don't really want to hear about that, I can see from your application what experience you have". Overall it was not a nice experience, the interviews seemed very cold and made me feel like I was wasting their time, one even yawned loudly in my interview and sat slumped on the table for the majority of the time unless he was asking a question himself.

Keele A100 **From the university:**

MMIs : New for 2013 entry

We are changing the format of our interviews to multiple mini interviews (MMIs), where candidates undertake a series of short interview stations. The stations will examine a range of skills and aptitudes. The format of stations may vary from a 1:1 traditional interview through to a role play.

All applicants are required to have undertaken work experience in a caring role; this need not be hospital or general practice-based.

We encourage applicants to tell us how they became involved in such work, for how long, how much time they spend each week, and most importantly what they gained from it.

King's College London A100 **From the university:**

Normally a 15 to 20 minute semi-structured interview. Interviewees complete a short questionnaire. Skills considered are:

- communication skills
- exploring in detail the interviewee's written application
- exploring general social and ethical issues
- the interviewee's general suitability for the programme and as a health professional
- how the interviewee will contribute to the College.

The aim of the interview is to assess your personal qualities and to find out whether you have the potential to become a successful member of the medical profession. Strong interpersonal and communication skills are most important, particularly when you consider the relationships which medical professionals need to build with their patients.

King's College London A102 **From the university:**

GPEP interviews will adopt the MMI system. Interviewees circulate from one timed station to another. At each station candidates meet one or two interviewers who ask structured questions and mark the responses to the questions independently. MMI is similar in style (but not content) to the short objective structured clinical examinations (OSCE) used in medical school assessment.

King's College London A100 From the candidates:

10 minute interview with 2 interviewers. Very friendly with a lot of emphasis on personal statement, work experience and recent news.

Also questions such as

- How do we know you're a team player?
- Why do you want to do medicine?

There was an ethical dilemma about a colleague who seemed to be losing motivation as a doctor, arriving late to meetings, not seeming themselves, what would you do.

Another ethical dilemma was; parents don't want child to receive a blood transfusion which will be potentially life-saving. What should you do?

We were given a written questionnaire to fill in before the interview which was discussed during the interview e.g. something you were proud of achieving recently.

Lancaster University A105 **From the university:**

Lancaster Medical School is currently home to a collaborative venture with the University of Liverpool to deliver undergraduate medical education in North Lancashire and Cumbria but has recently applied to the General Medical Council (GMC) for approval to deliver a medical degree programme independently from the University of Liverpool. The outcome of this application will be announced at the end of October 2012.

Since 2010, Lancaster has used the Multiple Mini Interview (MMI). The MMI consists of 12 different stations, most of which will be 5 minutes long. Some of the stations will consist of a short interview, where you will be asked questions related to your career choice. At other, you may be asked to read a short paragraph or watch a short video clip, take notes and then discuss at a subsequent station. An additional 20 minute station will involve group work and will assess your suitability for our problem-based learning curriculum. The applicant's performance in each station is assessed, against clearly defined criteria, by trained interviewers, including academic members of the University staff, NHS clinicians, local GPs and members of Local NHS trusts.

University of Leeds A100

From the university:

MMIs : New for 2013 entry

The interview will be in a multiple mini-interview (MMI) format. MMIs will be used for the first time in 2012. The questions and tasks in the interview are designed to gain further insight into the applicant's personal qualities and some cognitive skills. Scores from each station in the MMI will be collated to achieve an overall rating of the applicant.

There will be 8 stations in total. Criteria assessed would be:

- Motivation/Insight
- Areas of responsibility
- Ethics
- Social awareness

There will be scenarios and possibly some role-play.

University of Leicester A100 From the university:

MMI, first used for 2012 entry, assesses

- Verbal communication
- Written communication
- Listening
- Problem solving
- Review of personal statement

University of Leicester A101 From the university:

MMI, first used for 2012 entry, assesses

- Verbal communication
- Written communication
- Listening
- Problem solving

University of Leicester A100 From the candidates:

MMI, 6 stations, 8 minutes per station, 2 minutes break in between stations to prepare, and read a brief summary of each station.

- Asked about personal statement, pros and cons of medicine, and your own flaws.
- Mathematical reasoning station. Basic maths, such as 120 x 60, given a calculator, and noise cancelling headphones. Questions set out as a medical scenario, and you had to work out dosages, etc.
- Read an article (on social media in medicine) and had to answer comprehension questions on the article.

- Role Play. You are on work experience and the doctor asks you to talk with a patient while he waits to go in. the aim is to get as much information about his life as you can.
- More standard style questioning on teamwork.
- You are given a four minute video on a doctor asking a patient questions on a backache, and you have 8 minutes to write useful notes on the video. You are assessed on legibility, clarity and how much information you got.

In previous years (before MMI) questions have included:

- Why medicine?
- Tell us about yourself?
- What work experience have you had?
- What do you know about C. Difficile?
- Approx length of interview(s)20 mins
- If a doctor told you they were thinking about giving up medicine what would you say?
- What type of medicine would you like to go into?
- What is the career path of that speciality?
- Does a doctor always have to be the team lead?
- Why medicine?
- What will you do if you don't get into medicine this year?

University of Liverpool A100 &A101

From the university:

Applicants are invited to an approximately 15 minute, semi-structured interview with 2 people drawn from a panel of trained interviewers, including academic members of the University staff, NHS clinicians, GPs and members of Local NHS trusts. The structure of the interview and the assessment criteria used are the same for A100 and A101 applicants. The criteria used to assess the interview are

- Knowledge of the Liverpool medical programme and its curriculum
- Medical ethics
- Team work
- Healthcare career awareness and insight
- Caring for the local community
- Critical, coherent and informative approach to communication

University of Liverpool A100

From the candidates:

Short 15 minute interview including questions such as;

- Why medicine?
- Why Liverpool?
- What will make you a good doctor?
- There is a patient who wants to end their life; how would you react to this situation?
- What do you know about the course? What is bad about PBL?

University of Manchester A106 **From the university:**

The aim of the interview is to explore the non-academic criteria as well as to encourage applicants to talk naturally about themselves, their studies and their experiences, and to demonstrate that they have the interpersonal skills to be able to communicate effectively and show that they are well-rounded individuals:

- 30 minute group task with up to 9 candidates discussing a medical scenario. The first ten minutes will be allocated to individual thought; the remaining time will be spent trying to reach consensus within the group. We do not expect you to have any more than a layperson's general knowledge of the medical issues.
- One-to-one interviews of 8 minutes each at three separate stations, comprising:
    - Reflection on the group discussion.
    - Discussion surrounding personal statement.
    - Discussion of issues from a wider nature in the fields of medicine.

Ability to communicate

Communication skills are essential to the practice of almost all aspects of medicine. We expect candidates to be able to express their ideas clearly and coherently and to be able to follow a reasoned argument. Candidates who give spontaneous yet well-thought-out answers are more likely to impress the interviewers than those who give obviously rehearsed and 'coached' responses.

Why do you want to be a doctor?

This is an obvious but vital question. We will seek specific evidence of the experiences which have influenced your decision to study medicine.

Previous caring experience

Your experiences in a caring role will be of great interest. These need not be in a traditional mainstream medical environment. The interview is an opportunity for candidates to relate not only to the facts and details of their experiences, but also their emotional responses to them and what they have gained from them.

Matters of a medical interest

The interviewers will expect you to have an intelligent layperson's view on contemporary aspects of medicine particularly those of current media interest.

Ethical and other issues

Ethical issues may be raised by the interviewers, but only to assess your ability to coherently summarise the issues at stake. Candidates should be reassured that neither the interviewers nor the Medical School will take a position on any ethical issue. It is not the candidate's ethical views that the interviewers may be interested in, but how coherently the candidate expresses the ethical dilemmas facing medical practitioners. Candidates will not be asked questions in any of the following areas: gender, sexuality, marital or parental status, race, religion, social background.

University of Manchester A106 From the candidates:

Team work: We were given 10 min reading time. The scenario was an elderly man with corneal dystrophy with 3 different treatment options. Each group member was given some specific information, e.g. success rate of an operation, or details relating to his family. We had 20 min to work together to make a definite choice. They stressed that the decision was of no importance and that we were being tested on how well we worked as a team.

3 stations: The man conducting the personal statement station was quite tough and tried to question as many parts of the statement as possible. The next station involved giving positive and negative points of our own performance in the group task as well as for the team as whole. At the final station one question; "do you think the internet is having a positive or negative effect on health?" and for another candidate a question relating to cholesterol and exercise and what could be done to persuade people to exercise. Another candidate had a moral question regarding your boss (consultant) having a relationship with a girl under 16; what would you do?

All of us noticed that the man conducting the personal statement interview was playing a sort of "bad cop" role however as soon as the interview finished he was extremely nice so applicants should not panic if the interviewer seems unimpressed.

Newcastle A100 & A101 **From the university:**

The interview will be conducted by two selectors and will last approximately 25 minutes. Interviews will assess:

- Why you have chosen Newcastle.
- Your reflection on commitment to care and the role of a doctor. This will cover commitment to care of others; insight into a career and the role of a doctor; understanding the NHS and ethical issues.
- Your reflection on your personal attributes. This will cover learning styles; communication skills; fluency and ability to deal with questions; ability to explain a specific concept; non academic and personal interests; personal attributes.
- Verification of your Personal Statement. Ability to verify their personal statement, drawing on examples therein and expanding on them.
- Your overall performance at interview.

Newcastle University A100 **From the candidates:**

Panel of 2 doctors. 25 minute interview. Very friendly and relaxed and focused mostly around what was said in my personal statement:

- Why medicine? Why Newcastle?
- Qualities of a good doctor?
- What qualities do you have which would make you a good doctor?
- How have you dealt with a stressful situation?
- How did you get here?
- How do you fit in all that you do?

- How do you relax?
- Proudest achievement?
- Details relating to work experience.
- Started the interview by asking how I got there and then asked about journey to apply to medicine.
- Talked about being caring so they asked why I did not apply for nursing.
- Are surgeons the most important people in a hospital?
- What difficult issues did you see on work experience?
- Why I had applied to Newcastle.
- What do you know about the course.
- How is the NHS funded?
- Should smokers be supported on the NHS?
- Senario – you turn up for work still drunk following a heavy night what would you do?

I had spent some time abroad with some HIV patients:
- What is the difference between HIV and other viruses?
- Scenario question: I don't know anything about science explain to me about HIV and continued questioning me on this topic, went on to ask me what a retro virus was and why HIV is so bad.

I play tennis and was asked to:
- Explain the rules of tennis
- Asked if I had read anything interesting in a magazine I had cited in my personal statement.

Nottingham A100 **From the university:**

Semi-structured interviews. The aim is to identify applicants who are academically able enough to cope with the course, are motivated towards a career in medicine, have insight into the implications of this career choice and who have or appear to have the potential to acquire the personal skills expected of medical practitioners. The interview will normally be conducted by two senior staff, one of whom will be a member of the Admissions Committee and will act as chairperson. The interview will last approximately 15 minutes and applicants will be questioned on these themes:

- Motivation
- Empathy
- Communication skills
- Personality

Nottingham A101 **From the university:**

You will be interviewed by clinicians, academics and a lay person, in a multiple mini interview format. Lay people will be drawn from a wide range of professions allied to medicine, science, health services management, education and human resources. You will be graded on your answers to questions based around:

- Are you realistic about what it means to be a doctor?
- Your interest in the field of medicine
- Your personal attributes necessary for the study and practice of medicine

Nottingham A100 **From the candidates:**

I had an interview with two clinicians, an anaesthetist and A&E, and a silent observer, which lasted 15 minutes.

- Why do you want to be a doctor?
- Why medicine?
- What are the qualities of a doctor?
- Why not bio-medicine?
- What is empathy?
- Give a scenario where you have used empathy
- Tell me about your work experience
- Give an example of team work. What do you do if something goes wrong in your team?
- Tell me about the European Working Times Directive and any problems it has caused.
- What is the role of a doctor?
- What is the worst part of being a doctor?
- How do you cope with stress?
- This led onto a discussion about sports
- Has a friend ever approached you with a problematic dilemma?
- Why Nottingham?

Two scenarios with about 5 – 10 seconds thinking time:

- I was working in A & E and had heard that there had been a robbery yesterday and that a man with a specific description had been stabbed in the right leg. In comes a man who vaguely fits the description with a wound in his right leg that looked like a stab wound but states he had an accident, what should you do?

- Before an exam my friend says he is scared about the exam but has hidden some cheat notes in his pocket, what do you do? After you find out that you have failed and that he has got a great mark and is boasting about it, what do you do? They were quite pushy on this one but kept emphasising there was no right answer.
- You are in third year medical school (clinical year based in hospital) and find out your roommate (also third year) is taking drugs (you find needles in the bathroom). What do you do?
- What would you do if you had to deal with a patient you didn't like?

Nottingham A101 **From the candidates:**

MMI. Six minutes for each of the eight stations, with two minutes break in between each station.

- The interviewer is pretending to be your employee. You have to tell them that, due to cutbacks, you need to terminate their employment, even though they have been working satisfactorily for you for years.
- Ethics: what are they and are they black and white? How does ethics relate to medicine?
- Why Nottingham University and what do you know about the structure of the course?
- Health issues facing society today
- Work experience and what did you learn about yourself?
- Work experience and did you feel part of a team when you were shadowing doctors?

- Stress: How do you cope with it? Do you think studying for medicine will be stressful and if so, why?
- Tell the interviewer, who is pretending to be your patient, that you have given them the wrong drug. The interviewer reacts badly so you have to respond accordingly.
- Advantages / Disadvantages of medicine
- What are your strengths?
- Why Nottingham?
- Where have you seen good teamwork in your work experience?
- How should doctors treat other healthcare professionals?
- What do you understand by PBL and the advantages and disadvantages?
- Give an example of where you had to deal with a lot of stress and how did you manage?
- Is the doctor the most important member of a team?
- Recent news story where doctor made a mistake.
- Fellow student you discover is taking drugs/alcohol how would you act and what would you do?
- Terminally ill patient only wants to donate organs to Christians, explain to him that on that premise you cannot accept his organs.

Oxford University A100 **From the university:**

Personal characteristics:

- Empathy: ability and willingness to imagine the feelings of others and understand their reasons
- A well-informed and strong desire to practise medicine
- Communication: ability to make knowledge and ideas clear using language appropriate to the audience
- Honesty and integrity
- Ethical awareness
- Ability to work with others
- Capacity for sustained and intense work

Oxford University A101 **From the university:**

Selection Criteria:

- A clear commitment to medicine
- A realistic attitude to the subject
- Curiosity about the scientific basis of medicine
- An ability to listen and to communicate
- Be able to win the trust of colleagues and patients.
- A mature and professional attitude.
- Evidence of self-motivation
- Ability to organize life and work
- Ability to develop good relationships with other people
- A high level of communication skills
- An interest in and an ability to communicate with people from all backgrounds
- Personal integrity
- Stability of character

- Leadership potential
- Concern for the welfare of others.

Oxford University A101 **From the candidates:**

3 interviews, each with 2 interviewers, each 20 mins long
The first interview was a personal interview:

- Why medicine? Why Oxford?
- About myself, what I enjoy
- What skills I've learnt from my experience
- What responsibility I've had.

This interview was a really good discussion about my experiences, what has led me to want to do medicine and to Oxford, about my hobbies, what I got involved in at university. They were far more open than Cambridge; they probed the answers that I gave, asked for more examples, asked for different perspectives, challenged what I said, encouraged me to challenge them, it was generally a really positive experience.
The second interview was more science and ethics based, with some questions about the NHS. This was more challenging.
The third interview was the next day at another college. They tore me apart. We started with a scientific paper, provided for pre-interview reading. The first part of the interview was based on the paper. Then they asked me about DNA and other random things. But it must have been OK because I got an offer!

Peninsula University **From the university:**

In January 2012 the two founding members of the Peninsula College of Medicine and Dentistry (PCMD) the Universities of Exeter and Plymouth, outlined their plans to expand independently and grow the success of the now nationally recognised professional health education provider.

These changes will come into effect at the start of the 2013 Academic Year.

Peninsula University **From the candidates:**

We were given 20 minutes to prepare a scenario about a patient who refused to have life saving treatment when his family wanted him to have it. What are the main ethical issues raised by the scenario you have chosen of a patient refusing treatment? Also:

- Tell us about a time when you felt a great sense of achievement.
- What can severe stress lead doctors to do?
- Are you a team player?

We had to fill in a questionnaire prior to the interview asking questions like:

- Why medicine
- Why Peninsula
- What are the current issues for the NHS?

Plymouth University A100 From the university:

The interview is structured and formal to make sure every student is asked the same questions and receives the same prompts. It aims to explore your attitudes, outlook and way of thinking.

If you are selected for interview you need to show us you have the following essential qualities:

- Integrity
- Veracity and honesty
- Flexibility
- Motivation and commitment
- Pro-social attitudes e.g. students who show empathy and who are non-judgmental
- Communication skills, including listening
- Potential for leadership
- Students who show insight into what it is to be a doctor
- The ability to be a team player
- The ability to deal with stress appropriately
- Problem solving skills
- Students who know their limitations, their strengths and weaknesses
- Reflectiveness
- Students who demonstrate a suitable approach to life and people

Plymouth University A100 From the candidates:

See Peninsula

Queen Mary (Barts) A100 From the university:

Normally two members of senior academic or clinical staff and sometimes a lay selector assessing:

- Motivation and realistic approach to medicine
- Show initiative, resilience and maturity
- Work well as part of a team
- Be well organised and able to problem solve
- Likely contribution to university life
- Communicate effectively in a wide range of situations

Queen Mary (Barts) A101 From the university:

(NB Joint with Warwick) The Selection Centre lasts half a day and takes place in February. Trained assessors will observe you completing tasks including a group-based task, written exercise and structured interview.

Queen Mary (Barts) A100 From the candidates:

The interview panel had two clinical doctors involved with academic teaching. The interview started by asking me about a pre-released article (see below), then:

- Why medicine? Why Barts?
- What personal qualities does a doctor need to possess and how have you shown these qualities?
- What I might be the negative side to working as a doctor. This led into a conversation about patient death and I was also asked how doctors cope.
- My understanding of medical career progression.

Given a newspaper article ten days before the interview about 'saviour sibling twins' and asked to consider it.

There was a very relaxed atmosphere before the interviews. There were many interviews taking place in the large room at the same time separated by panel boards. You could therefore hear the other interviews taking place which was a bit off putting.

What are the most common illnesses in the east end?
Two weeks before the interview we were sent an article by Archbishop Dr Sentamu entitled *Assisted Suicide: There must be no slippery slope*. Asked what I thought.

Queen Mary (Barts) A101 From the candidates:

(NB Joint with Warwick) We were put into groups of five, had a teamwork exercise, a written exercise, and then commenting on a recorded interview and also:

- Why medicine?
- How have you changed your communication style during your work experience?
- What are some of the challenges about being a doctor and how would you deal with them?

Written exercise, asking you to prioritise several scenarios, including a student cheating at medical school, a pupil who has been late to class, a pupil who got a paper published and should be rewarded, and a pupil with family problems.

Queen's University Belfast A100 From the university:

Nine station multiple mini interview (MMI) to determine non-cognitive performance. MMIs are being used to test non-cognitive competence and the applicant's personal statement is considered within this process.

These interviews have been designed to test the following which have been identified by both patients and academic staff as key non-cognitive competencies for medicine:

- Empathy
- Problem-solving
- Moral reasoning
- Communication skills

Sample interview station 1

You the candidate are asked to assume you are a first year medical student and that on your way home from class you reach a bus stop. At the bus stop a class mate is sitting there looking glum, obviously upset. You don't know their name. Demonstrate how you would approach this situation. Your classmate will be waiting at the bus stop when you enter the station.

This station has been designed to test the candidate's ability to communicate and to demonstrate empathy.

Sample interview station 2

Your mother rings you and asks you to come round and help with a major family decision. Her 70 year old father has been diagnosed with a condition that will kill him sometime in the next five years. He can have a procedure that will correct the disease and not leave him with any long term problems, but the procedure has a 10% mortality rate. He wants to have the procedure but your mother is not in favour of it. How would you help mediate this issue?

Non Cognitive competencies being assessed:

- Problem solving
- Ethical reasoning
- Communication

Aim of the question (seen by the interviewer only) to find out if the candidate:

- Demonstrates sensitivity to the needs of others
- Understands the right of the patient to be fully involved in decisions about their care
- Can think of ways to help resolve a situation when emotional issues may cloud one's judgement
- Understands the limit of their own knowledge and experience

University of Sheffield A100 From the university:

A standard interview lasting around 25 minutes with 3 people. One will be a doctor, the second a final year medical student and the third either another doctor or academic within the Medical School.

The questioning at interview is based around the following criteria:

- knowledge of and interest in study in Sheffield
- motivation for medicine
- evidence of commitment for caring
- depth & width of interests communication skills
- understanding the nature of medicine
- medical work experience.

You can expect the panel to ask you about your UCAS application. You should also keep up to date with recent medical breakthroughs, topical controversies, ethical issues and NHS politics. Your appearance at interview is important. You should dress appropriately and in a professional manner.

University of Sheffield A100 From the candidates:

Interviewed by 2 doctors for 35 minutes. While walking to the interview I was asked how I got to the medical school. At interview I was asked

- Why medicine? Why Sheffield?
- What do you know about Sheffield as a city?
- Who is famous from Sheffield?

- Why do you want to be a doctor?
- What have you learnt from your work experience?
- How do you deal with learning things you don't enjoy?
- Why are you not doing a fourth A2?
- Asked to define the different types of euthanasia and assisted suicide and what was legal in this country.
- Asked about the ethics surrounding mental health.
- Asked how I would cope with stress.
- Asked about my work experience which led into seeing good medical practice and what to do when you find yourself out of your depth.
- Asked what I should do as a junior doctor if I have seen bad medical practice by another doctor.
- Asked about MDT meetings and how they are run.
- Nearly all questions were about the NHS and the health service (another candidate said there were no NHS or news related questions.)
- Have you encountered any ethical situations during your work experience?

Make sure you know about your chosen university and its course, highlight key aspects of the course you like. Also mention the fact you went on their open day. A lot of questions weren't specifically about my work experience but seemed to be designed to allow me to answer the question using my work experience. One member of the committee made comments about gap years in a negative way. I wondered if this was to see how the candidate would react.

University of Southampton A100 & A101

From the university:

Southampton rarely interview

University of Southampton A100

From the candidates:

Relatively informal and casual. More like a conversation with 2 interviewers. Started off with general questions like:

- Why medicine?
- Why Southampton?
- The 2 interviewers read my personal statement beforehand, so they asked me a few questions about it – basically more detail about my experiences and what they taught me.
- What are 3 essential qualities of a doctor.
- Name one situation when you had to overcome a problem
- Any medical news I heard about recently.
- The only clinical scenario asked: If a patient spoke in a language that you do not know, how would you communicate with the patient?

Very relaxed atmosphere, especially because Southampton doesn't interview most applicants (I am an international applicant). The current medical students who talk to you before the interview are very helpful.

University of St Andrews A100

From the university:

The interview lasts 20 minutes and assesses your potential as a doctor and provides you with an opportunity to demonstrate your ability to think critically and with insight on a range of topics related to a medical career.

Communication skills are essential to the practice of almost all aspects of medicine. We expect candidates to be able to express their ideas clearly and coherently and to be able to follow a reasoned argument. Just before your interview you will be asked to read a short article on a medically related topic for about 10 minutes. The interview panel will then ask you questions about the article. They will be assessing your comprehension and ability to summarise as well as communication skills.

The panel will expect the candidate to have a general understanding of the St Andrews course. In particular, we expect candidates to be aware of the way in which we deliver the Medical programme and to have an opinion on its appeal to them, its advantages and limitations.

The interview panel will be interested in how you have prepared yourself for entering into a medical career. They will be keen to know what you have gained from work experience in a medical or 'caring' environment or any other environment that you feel has been relevant in preparing you for a career in medicine.

St George's A100 & A101 **From the university:**

MMIs are a way of assessing applicants through a series of different, short interviews and activities. Applicants will spend 5 minutes in each of 7 stations. MMIs are short focused interactions which combine traditional style questions with task-based questions such as:

- Pack a suitcase for a trip, where the case can only contain half of the items available
- Travelling on the London Underground, one of your friends has become separated from the group – it's their first time in London – describe your plan of action
- You have a list of 15 individuals, giving their sex, age and occupation – you can save five of them from nuclear attack – which five and why?
- As captain of a football team, inform a member of your team that they have not been selected to play
- Inform your neighbour that you have just (accidentally) run over and killed their cat

The tasks assess one or more of:

- Academic ability and intellect
- Empathy
- Initiative and resilience
- Communication skills
- Organisation and problem solving
- Team work
- Insight and integrity
- Effective learning style

St George's A100 & A101 **From the candidates:**

The buzzer sounds 30 seconds before the end of the station.

- Why do you want to be a doctor as opposed to any other health care professional?
- There was a small problem solving task using basic mathematical skills. Why do you think we gave you a problem solving task?
- How would you recommend spending money on good care whilst ensuring minimum spending?
- You are a baker, 6 weeks ago an order was taken, it was not put into the system, customer has arrived to pick up order, what do you do?
- How would you deal with criticism?
- What from your work experience has confirmed your desire to do medicine?
- What is the most important medical discovery in the last 10 years?

The interview room is fairly small with 7 booths set up, you have to stand outside your booth for a minute then enter for 5 minutes where you will be asked one question, they cannot ask anything else but I found that a couple asked me prompting questions towards the end.

- Q1. (ice breaker) What attributes will you need to study here and for the future and why do you think you have those? Q2. What do you think has made the biggest improvement to medicine and patients in the last 150 years and why is research important?

- You are the leader of a PBL session and 2 members who have been in a long term relationship are arguing loudly with each other, what would you do?
- A meeting overseas which could influence your career. You have been given a budget of £100, the meeting starts at 10:00, time difference is 2 hours and you get severely sea sick, what option do you take? A. Luxury train with an executive booth for £115 takes 90mins and leaves the UK at 06:55. B. catch a ride in a car with a friend who has the ferry booked, he is asking for £20 and thinks he will arrive at 09:30. C. Get a plane that leaves 17:30 the night before costing £95 takes an hour, and then a hotel for £45.
- What can doctors and patients do to make finances go further in medicine?
- You volunteered to look after your neighbour's pet rabbit, while you were cleaning out his cage he escaped, you didn't call your neighbour while he was away, so now he is back go round to explain.
- You are working as a registrar in a busy ward, and you find out the due to your misdiagnosis a patient who was 53 has died, how would you deal with this situation and who would you turn to for support?
- What qualities have you gained from your work experience and how do they relate to medicine?

Other candidates have been asked:

- Why medicine rather than another healthcare profession and what skills will you need to improve when at medical school?
- What are the advantages and disadvantages of NICE?

- How would you deal with a patient who wanted to make a complaint?
- How has your work experience prepared you?
- Research in the last 25 years that you have found interesting - this one had leading questions e.g. I talked about the human genome project, then mid sentence she asked, What's a gene? I spoke to the others in my group and this happened to all of them.
- How would you deal with somebody who isn't pulling their weight in the PBL group?
- You are going on a business trip between Southampton and Paris and there are 3 routes to take but 3 issues (cost, wheelchair bound colleague, timing) all about priority and then they asked us why they asked this question?
- Advantages and disadvantages of medicine
- Work experience and how it contributed to decision to study medicine
- Significant medical breakthroughs in last 50 years
- Why is the NHS budget increasing even though health standards are improving?
- Tell examiner to tie shoelace using only words.
- Break the bad news to an athlete to tell her that her knee hadn't recovered and she couldn't run in Olympics. Clock starts as soon as you start reading scenario sheet.

Swansea University A101 From the university:

The interview will be structured to ascertain your personal attributes, qualities, suitability and potential not only to complete the course successfully, but also to pursue a successful career in medicine, as set out by the GMC's Standards in *'Tomorrows Doctors'*.

Swansea University A101 From the candidates:

30 minute informal 'chat'

- Why do you want to be a doctor?
- Why Swansea?
- Can you tell me about the learning technique at Swansea and how it compares to other styles?
- Can you tell me about the progression from medical school, F1 and F2 to doctor?
- When you were at University tell me about a situation where you had to work as part of a team and what role did you play?
- I see you have volunteered at a Hospice, did this make you sad?
- Do you think all hospitals should have a ward/department dedicated to patients who have suffered from strokes?
- What attributes should a good doctor have?
- Did anything in my work experience nearly put me off applying to medicine?
- What is bad about a 4 year course?

The last to be interviewed had to wait for over 5 hours.

University College London A100 From the university:

Interviews last approximately 15-20 minutes and are conducted by a panel of 2-3 interviewers, including clinical and basic medical science staff, a senior medical student or 'lay' interviewer (e.g. Head of Sixth Form, guest GP). Interviewees will be given a copy of their BMAT essay prior to the interview. Interviewers score the candidate for the following qualities:

- Intellectual ability (intellectual curiosity and robustness)
- Motivation for (and understanding of) a career in medicine
- Awareness of scientific and medical issues
- Ability to express and defend opinions, including discussion of BMAT essay topic
- Attitude, including flexibility and integrity
- Individual strengths (e.g. social, musical, sporting interests or activities)
- Communication skills (verbal and listening)

University College London A100 From the candidates:

3 interviewers but only 2 spoke, and the interview lasted 15 minutes. The questions were very generic, such as

- Why do you want to be a doctor?
- What are the good qualities for a doctor to have?

There were no science questions.

University College London A101 From the candidates:

- Why UCL? Why medicine?
- What do you know about IT and the NHS?

- How could the IT system change in the future?
- What are disadvantages of robotics in medicine?
- What is the role of a GP?
- Questions relating to personal statement – they know your statement inside out.
- Discuss something interesting from your work experience.
- What do patients look for in a good doctor?
- What do you do to relieve stress?
- What politics exist between patient and doctor?
- Why has life expectancy improved drastically in the last 100 years?
- Anything interesting in the news lately?
- What do you know about screening? Anything in the news recently that was related to Screening?
- Questions relating to BMAT essay, why I had picked it and what I would change.

Interviewers are really friendly and even made jokes. I'd say this was an atypical interview, however, it was made easier by the fact that you were asked many questions based on your personal statement. They will be observing the candidates in the waiting room at some points for instance when talking to other candidates.

University of Warwick A101 From the university:

Warwick and Barts operate a joint selection centre; group task, written exercise and interview to assess:

- empathise with patients
- communicate effectively in different situations
- treat others in a caring manner
- work well as part of a team
- organise and problem solve
- show initiative and resilience
- develop self-directed learning styles

You can discover whether you have these qualities through caring work experience; perhaps as a ward volunteer, at a school, as an auxiliary nurse or first aider.

University of Warwick A101 From the candidates:

Watched a 5 minute patient-doctor consultation video then:

- What was good about the doctor's communication?
- What was bad about the doctor's communication?
- Did he demonstrate empathy? How? What else could he have done?

Personal questions:

- Why do you want to be a doctor?
- Tell me where you demonstrated empathy.
- Why is the time right for you to study medicine now?
- What work experience have you done and what have you learnt from it?

- Tell me about a time where you have had to alter the way in which you communicate to people.
- What do you know about different learning styles?
- What extra-curricular activities do you do?
- How do you manage stress?

Written exam: asked to prioritise scenarios and why.

- a girl has be signing in her friend for lectures
- a girl who is normally a hard working student has been late for lectures.
- a boy wants to enter the Commonwealth Games but will have to miss 3 weeks of term, and an exam.
- a boy has had an article published and the university want to put it in their newsletter but he is embarrassed.

The group task: Groups of 4 with an examiner assigned to watch. We had paper, a compass, a ruler, some stands and clamps and some string. We had 20 minutes to make a wind up car travel a metre at a height of a metre. After the 20 minutes a medical student measured the length our car travelled and then gave us a battery (to increase the weight of the car) and then gave us 10 more minutes to see if we could alter our 'bridge' to carry the extra weight.

I am sure that Warwick are looking for you to not only provide sensible answers but I also think that the selection day is structured to allow you to exhibit as much of your character and personality as possible. I think they just want to know that you are a nice person as well as an appropriate applicant.

The MMI Interview

The interview is a chance to impress the selectors with qualities that cannot easily be scored or quantified on paper. As such, we will discuss here not only final preparation and practice for MMI, but also the concepts, attitudes and experiences which you should have dwelt on in the months, if not years, preceding any interview.

You will often hear that preparing for interview can be a risky activity. Preparation is a broad term which covers everything from work experience to practicing answers. Good preparation allows you to express your personal qualities. The concern of admissions tutors does not relate so much to preparation as to 'coaching'. Preparation and practice is undertaken by successful candidates, whilst coaching can be counterproductive, and copying other people's answers will not make you stand out. Coaching implies that candidates are primed with 'correct' answers. There is hardly ever a single correct answer, regurgitation is rarely endearing, and coached candidates may not have the skills to answer all questions. We encourage preparation and practice.

What are the schools looking for?

Candidates should be focused on the fact that they are applying for a career, not just a degree. The Medical Schools

Council published the *'Guiding Principles for the Admission of Medical Students'*, which guides schools in the selection and admission of students to medical schools. This document was revised in 2010 in collaboration with the Admission Deans from the UK's medical schools.

The guiding principles in the document include:

- Selection for Medical School implies selection for the medical profession.
- The aim is to select those with the greatest aptitude for medical training from those with high academic ability.
- The practice of medicine requires the highest standards of professional and personal conduct.
- Failure to declare information that has a material influence on a student's fitness to practise may lead to termination of their medical course.
- The practice of medicine requires the highest standards of professional competence.
- The primary duty of care is to patients.
- Applicants should demonstrate some understanding of what a career in medicine involves and their understanding of, and suitability for, a caring profession.
- The Role of the Doctor Consensus Statement, 2008, outlines the attributes doctors require.

The full document can be found on the Medical Schools Council website, *www.medschools.ac.uk*, where you can also view their Role of the Doctor Consensus Statement, which is also referred to on a number of school websites.

Other documents which you should aim to access are the schools' departmental Admissions Policies. Most schools provide a link to these on their website, although not always in the most obvious place. Many candidates we meet do not know about admissions policies, and most have not read them for their chosen schools. These policies often provide the precise selection criteria against which applications are scored, often for both personal statements and interviews.

To name but a few, the qualities sought include:

Genuine interest in Medicine

- Commitment to medicine
- Motivation towards a medical career
- Realistic view of the role of a doctor
- Appreciation of the medical school's course design

Personal attributes

- Communication (written, listening and speaking)
- Communication with people of different backgrounds
- Communication of difficult information
- Broad social, cultural or sporting interests
- A well-rounded personality
- Empathy, compassion and patience
- Caring attitude and concern for welfare of others
- Non judgemental
- Interest in people
- A respect for people's rights, dignity and opinions
- Integrity
- What you can offer the medical school

- Ability to self-criticise and know one's strengths and weakness
- Humility and an open mind

Skills

- Academic knowledge
- Willingness to keep updated
- Ability to discuss important issues in medicine
- Capacity for self-directed knowledge acquisition
- Willingness to accept responsibility
- Practical Skills
- Ability to learn and implement new ideas and skills
- Organisational skills
- Non-academic accomplishments
- Problem-solving skills

Team player

- Recognition of other health professionals' roles
- Teamwork
- Leadership

Coping under stress

- Recognition of the stresses in medicine
- Recognition of stress in oneself and others
- Ability to recognise limitations
- Strategies for coping

General Tips for approaching Interviews

Tidy up your thoughts

Think of your personal experiences and write down examples of when you have demonstrated the different qualities the schools are looking for. Consider creating a table with the common qualities required and examples from your experiences for each attribute. Your best experience is often applicable to more than one of the qualities, but it is useful to have different examples for each so that you don't have to use the same experience twice. Doing this written exercise may enable you to recall useful experiences in the pressure of the moment. Looking at communication for example:

	Communication 1
Situation	When working in the hospice, talking with a patient who had a hearing difficulty
Action	At first just spoke louder and slower - didn't work very well and disturbed other patients. Found out from patient if it was a long standing problem and if they had a hearing aid. They did, made sure it was working and had a battery in it and made sure patient was wearing it when we needed to communicate. Asked them what the best way of communicating with them was. Looked up best ways of communicating on the Royal Association for Deaf people website
Result and Reflection	First action was instinctive but not very effective. Best way of solving the problem was to involve patient. Will remember this when dealing with patients as a medical student and doctor
	Communication 2
Situation	When shadowing a GP in her clinic, GP explaining test results to a patient.

Action	GP found out what the patient's concerns were and what they knew already and what they wanted to know. Then told patient what the test results were and explained the interpretation without jargon. Checked the patient understood in a non patronising way. Explained what the next steps would be, involving the patient in the choice. Summarised the information again at the end. Gave time for patient to ask questions and interrupt.
Result	Patient upset at results but grateful to doctor for clear and supportive explanation
Reflection	I started to understand the aspects of good communication and how this can help make consultations a less distressing experience for the patient.

Practice discussing each of the required skills out loud and to anyone who will listen. Discuss why the skills are important. Do you have these skills? What is your evidence?

How to answer a question

A comprehensive answer is important in any interview, especially a structured one, and even more in an MMI. We will consider three aspects to help you present your response. Firstly, your form – here we mean the nature and quality of your speech as well as body language. Secondly, your structure – flow and categorisation. Thirdly, your content – the importance of comments that are accurate, relevant and supported with evidence.

Form

This is the hardest of the three aspects for you to analyse and even harder to correct, but fundamentally important. If you are inaudible, or sit and giggle, you will struggle to compete. The key here is to practice and get feedback. Everyone's opinion of your performance is valid – are you making sense? Can your interviewer visualise someone like you advising them on their medical care? Pay attention to your mother – if she has always scolded you for running your hands through your hair, now might be the time to consider that she might be right. Similarly, do not only seek advice from those people you are sure will give you only positive feedback, seek criticism too. The best person to approach is probably the one you are most embarrassed to ask! Ask a medical person to give you a practice interview. Some people choose to go to interview practice courses.

Structure

Structuring your answer is of particular importance in MMIs. As with any highly structured interview, the interviewers are likely to have a very limited number of questions to ask in each station. Indeed, at its extreme, interviewers may ask one, and only one question, and require you to fill the time appropriately. Pause to think; the gaping pause you feel will not seem as long to the interviewers, who will respect you for thinking about their well-thought-out question. Feel free to say "I will just think about that for a moment." Even if you are not surprised by the question, still pause. Rather like the structure of an essay, consider giving an introduction outlining what you are about to say, followed by your evidence and then a conclusion or summary to finish your answer. Give a full response, try to give examples of your experiences, and reflect on them, i.e. what you learnt and what you might do differently next time. You might use the STARR approach given in the tables above. Signpost any change of subject (comparable with a new paragraph in an essay), for instance 'In contrast..,' or 'Another example would be...'

If there are lots of different aspects to your answer, you may find it helpful to categorize what you are about to say, for instance; 'There are 3 aspects to my answer – X,Y,Z. In terms of X,.......'. Chunking in this way makes your reply easier to follow, and gives you, and the interviewers, a framework in advance.

Avoid giving lists with no explanation. Anyone can state simple things. For instance, all candidates are likely to be able to state that communication is an important skill as a doctor. *You* could *describe* a doctor who has communicated well. Perhaps your doctor really listened to your concerns about your spots when you were a teenager. Or tell of the time when you witnessed sad news being broken well (or badly) to a relative. Or tell of the skills you identified in a doctor you shadowed who was particularly good at communication. This book cannot give you your personal examples, it can merely suggest that you have them and use them.

Content

Answer the question! If you give a pre-prepared answer to a different question you will score poorly. Pausing before answering will reduce the risk of this occurring. Pause, think, chunk your response, signpost your chunks, be yourself, be honest, and then stop. Do not verbally wander the recesses of your mind for something profound, just answer the question honestly. A common mistake is to list many examples with no reflection when the question asked for *an* example (which inherently requires some reflection). Similarly, for a question such as 'tell me about *a* medical news story', some candidates make the mistake of listing the basics of a *number* of stories and fail to do justice to any of them.

Many candidates do themselves a disservice by underselling themselves, or conversely try too hard to 'impress'. The interviewer is not so interested in which famous surgeons you have met, but what you have learnt from your experiences. Be proud of your experiences. Cherish them. If you have undertaken work experience, you will have gained an insight into people's lives, which is a privilege.

Be well-read in current affairs, medical ethics and research. Always consider the impact on patients. There are certain things you need to study:

- A couple of medical news stories, in depth
- Basic ethical principles of
    - Autonomy
    - Capacity
    - Confidentiality
    - End of life care

    - The ethos of the NHS
- The job of a junior doctor
- An insight into career paths within the NHS
- The structure of the NHS and basic understanding of the reforms

Many of these subjects are discussed in later chapters.

Common mistakes and things to bear in mind

Speaking too fast

Slowing down will not only help to avoid exhausting your interviewers, you will probably deliver your information more concisely and will automatically improve your form and structure.

Being defensive

A common mistake is to be defensive. For instance, some people answer the question 'why do you *want* to be a doctor' by explaining why they do not want to be a nurse or scientist. That isn't the question and you may inadvertently say something offensive if you try to explain what detracts you from another career.

Most candidates could have done better in some aspect of their application. Perhaps their GCSE grades could have been better, or work experience could have started sooner, or better work experience could have been obtained. Many candidates are applying for a second time. As with most things in life, being defensive is rarely attractive, as there are better ways to explain any shortcomings, if indeed there is anything to explain. If you have genuinely let yourself down in some regard, and need to discuss it, then you will be praised for taking a mature and reflective approach, showing that you understand how you could have done better, and why you do things differently now. For instance, if you are specifically asked at interview why your A-level results are so horribly bad, resist the temptation to offer defensive excuses. You might instead offer something along the lines of, "Well, there were family/personal problems for me at the time but ultimately I did not work hard enough and got the results I deserved." By accepting responsibility, you will demonstrate maturity, honesty and reflection.

For the graduates, sometimes when we have asked "why do you want to study medicine?" the question they appear to have heard was "why do you think you have got enough marbles left to do this, you old fool?" or "why on earth didn't you do this sooner". The decision to interview you means that your age does not preclude you from studying, and that lots of very wise, experienced (and old) people have decided that old folks like you can be just as valuable as the young ones. Older candidates need to show a greater degree of commitment, but that comes from enthusiasm and experience, not a defensive attitude and a biography of your failures. Why you didn't do medicine before is probably irrelevant. Also, remember to talk about the pull of medicine, rather than reasons for wanting to leave your current position. Be positive and respectful of past experiences.

Nervous habits

Interviews know that you will be nervous and really can take it into account, it's very normal and understandable, and often preferable to over-confidence. However, whilst you cannot stop yourself from going bright red, you can avoid nail biting, hair playing, neck scratching, mouth covering, hand wringing, ceiling gazing and up to a point, nervous laughing. Sit on your hands if necessary. Tie your hair back. Get rid of fiddly necklaces. Don't wear too tight a suit or too short a skirt. If you're going to start dripping with sweat, take a handkerchief. Remember also that interviewers get nervous too - they are only human. One of my interviewers later admitted that he had been tremendously nervous, because he knew that his decision might affect the rest of a person's life.

Not smiling

A fixed smile is horrid, of course, but if you are answering a question in which you are describing your enthusiasm for medicine, a cold, blank face does not help to convince the examiners of that enthusiasm. The key here is not so much to focus on your smile, but to be honest about your thoughts and feelings.

Being Arrogant

Some people may give the impression of arrogance by not being able to discuss different points of view. Try to show your understanding of different sides of the argument. Try to understand all aspects of a situation, show empathy to those involved, and be analytical. Derogatory comments often reflect greatest on the people making them. There is always something that you can learn from every situation. Similarly, take care with 'certainty' in any ethical dilemma. A dilemma is by definition a complex issue.

Being patronizing or conversely, too technical

Demonstrate your communication skills by pitching your answers appropriately. You should be introduced at the start of the interview. Try to remember each interviewer's profession; you may even be able to involve them in your answer more: "*I imagine you see that sort of thing in your department all the time.*"

Drawing a blank

You may really draw a complete blank on a question, for instance: "T*ell us about a time when you have had to take on responsibility.*" If you are genuinely at a loss, you might approach it by first apologizing for being unable to recall an example, but in all interviews, and especially in an MMI, you need to try to answer the question as best you can. Signpost that you are altering the question slightly *"Unfortunately I think my nerves are getting the best of me and I cannot remember an example. However, I do understand the importance of the question and I'd like to tell you about why doctors need to be able to take on responsibility....I saw the importance of this during my work experience...."*

Do not be fazed by people making notes/scores

Notes and scoring is simply part of a fair process. For goodness sake do not try to look at them! You are trying to embark on a career with necessarily high standards of professional conduct – you do not want to look like a cheat. Look at your interviewer instead.

Get a balance between being over or under prepared

There is an easy solution to being under prepared of course - prepare. If you are over prepared, try to relax, try to feel the emotions that you are describing. You do not want to be describing what a death during your work experience meant to you with a monotone voice. Similarly, long lists and scientific/medical abbreviations are not impressive. Be especially careful if there are lay people on the panel. Remain human and endearing.

The 'obvious' questions

There are some questions which you will already anticipate. You should prepare for these questions, of course, but remember to 'keep it real' by really describing the experiences; be vivid and enthusiastic in your response.

What makes a good doctor?

The qualities described at the start of this chapter should provide some ideas upon which to build your answer. However, do not simply recite a list – anyone can do that. Your answer should be framed in the light of your work experience and you should have developed your own understanding. If you develop examples from your experiences, you will demonstrate commitment and insight. Remember to structure and signpost you answer, for example:

"A good doctor needs to have a mixture of academic skills and softer skills. Academic skills include scientific knowledge and acumen, data analysis, interpretation of research and keeping up to date. Softer skills include communication, empathy, ability

to handle stress and sadness, and ability to handle responsibility." (Intro)

"I have been fortunate to see a number of good doctors during my work experience, at both a junior and senior level. Whilst shadowing a junior doctor at.....I saw how....(Evidence)

"Similarly I shadowed a consultant in....He was also a good doctor, in a different way, as the emphasis on his skills was different. For instance.......(Evidence)

"During my work experience I often thought about whether I have the skills I saw in those doctors. I believe that I have these skills and have started to use skills that I have learned in my care work." (Conclusion)

Why do you want to be a doctor?

We commonly see this question being answered poorly. Trying to be 'special' and saying what 'the interviewer wants to hear', can be a route to failure. People, and doctors in particular, can spot a load of bull a mile off. Don't pretend, exaggerate or lie. Your desire is highly unlikely to be particularly special (you're likely to fall into either the group who have been inspired by their personal experiences, or the group who would like a career involving both science and people). Your answer will be made special by demonstrating motivation, evidence, reflection, knowledge and enthusiasm, within the construct of work experience. This question should not be answered without significant reference to work experience. Whilst it is useful to draw on your skills and explain why you might make a good doctor, be careful not to change the question into 'Why would you be a good doctor?'

Compare the following two introductions to this question:

"I want to be a doctor because I find the practice of medicine the most inspiring and dramatic of careers. I look forward to making a real difference in people's lives. I have done lots of work experience with different Consultants at the top of their field, and they have all been very encouraging about what a great doctor I will make. I've been preparing for this for years. I've won many prizes at school, and I know I will do well at medical school. I am fascinated by surgery and would like to be a neurologist."

This answer sounds 'dramatic' and highlights the candidate's confidence and proven ability. However, there is in fact little substance. One hopes that this introduction would be fleshed out by work experience later, but so far the answer seems rather forced and arrogant. Indeed, the candidate is so far not really answering the question of why he wants to be a doctor, but more why he thinks he would be good at it. One is left with the feeling that his idea of making a difference is something unrealistic. The last sentence is at best curious, as a neurologist is a physician, not a surgeon.

Now see what you think of this introduction:
"Being a doctor combines my fascination of science and my desire to work with people. Medicine affords a wonderful combination of science and art; of applying often black and white evidence on a case by case basis in ways which are often grey. I look forward to making differences to people's lives; not in the dramatic way we might see on the TV but in much more realistic ways. For instance I would love to be the doctor who speaks kindly to relatives when their loved one is dying, or the

doctor who can explain a procedure so that the patient is that little bit less nervous than they might otherwise have been. I have spent time talking to patients during my care work, and feel very proud of the beneficial effect I had on them, and them on me."

There is little 'glamour' to this answer, but it seems very real and believable. The candidate is also answering the question. It is a realistic and kind answer, and is already reflective towards care work experience. This is a great introduction, and I would expect this candidate to then give some specific examples and a solid conclusion to make this answer excellent.

Tell us about a particularly stressful time in your life, work or personal, and how you coped with it.

Your interviewers are looking for more than a one sentence statement, especially in an MMI. They are looking for insight, and a demonstration of skills. Try to think of a good example - remember that everyone found their A-levels stressful; most candidates have something better that they can discuss. As a conclusion, it might be useful to explain why the experience is relevant to medicine. Don't pick an example where you *didn't* cope, unless you can demonstrate good reasons why things would be different now.

What pressures do you think doctors face in their professional and personal lives?

Your answer should be framed in the light of your work experience and you should have developed your own understanding and insight. Pressures that you may have witnessed, and can expand on, might include: hard work (as a student or doctor), hours worked, uncooperative/ ungrateful patients, difficult colleagues, death and suffering, management and political pressures (e.g. rationing), safety, relationship pressures, an increasingly litigious society, etc. For example:

"There are a lot of pressures facing doctors, and these pressures vary between person to person and between departments. Generally speaking, doctors work long and often unsociable hours. They are exposed to smells, sights and sounds which are not always pleasant. They are exposed to often unpleasant people, and that includes both staff and patients. The career path is long, with a lot of hurdles along the way.
I shadowed a junior doctor and most of his work wasn't doctor-like in the way that the Consultant's was. His bleep was constantly sounding, everyone seemed to want him to do things, for instance the nurse, his reg, the patients, the relatives, and he had a job list that was frighteningly long. He had to go to radiology, to other wards as well as take bloods, write drug charts and discharge paperwork. He was really calm though and this worked really well. When he became frazzled towards the end of the day, he became less efficient and less patient, but I think because he was generally so professional, people recognized his strain and helped him. He often went home late and I got the impression his girlfriend wasn't always terribly impressed.
The Consultant has different pressures. A surgeon I shadowed seemed to have clinics ending in one hospital when he was due in theatre in another. He had to teach, as well as be responsible. I was quite surprised how much control some of the managers

seemed to exert over him; much of his day seemed to be spent dealing with political problems within the hospital.
Both of them seemed to genuinely enjoy patient contact though. For the junior doctor particularly, this contact seemed to make everything else completely worthwhile."

What do *you* think to this answer? Do you think he is a good candidate? We did, and the schools did. Does this answer paint a picture in your mind? Have you shadowed a junior doctor? What did you see? This answer won't, and shouldn't be, your answer; but you should have one of your own that's equally realistic and considered. If you haven't shadowed a junior doctor, take a few hours now to try to organise this.

Why do you want to come to this school?

Candidates answer this question best if they have researched the school including the prospectus and open day. Schools are proud of their degree structure. You need to know (and like) their design. Is it PBL? Integrated? Opportunity for intercalation? Pre-clinical and clinical? Small or large? Lectures shared with biomeds etc? Many lectures or more self directed? Which hospitals might you go to for your clinical placements? When do these start? If there are questions here you cannot answer, you need to do more research before you apply, and certainly before your interview.

Current Affairs and Advances in Medicine

You may be asked if there is anything of a medical nature that has interested you in the news lately. You should have a good understanding of a few topics found in the newspapers – which is of course what patients read. Try to think about the different aspects of what you read – what does your topic mean to patients, relatives, doctors, NHS finances, public health, ethics and so on. Think about the importance of your chosen topic(s) to different groups and read about media topics from different perspectives, from *The Sun* to *Nature*. It is pointless to discuss news stories here as they wouldn't be news after the day of publication of this book. Don't rely on the last few days' newspapers; make sure your interest has developed beyond that.

For any story that you do read about, there is an absolutely fantastic resource on the NHS website:
http://www.nhs.uk/News/Pages/NewsIndex.aspx
This is a really useful guide to the science behind the headlines. It describes the original research in an intelligent, unbiased way.

Asking Questions of the Interviewer

An interviewer will often conclude the interview by inviting you to ask any questions. This is not an indication that you must. They are courteously providing you with an opportunity to ask a specific question, should you have one, and nothing else. Do not see it as an opportunity to give yourself more time and another opportunity to engage the interviewers in new detail. They will have another interview to do after you, and would probably rather get on with it, so avoid unnecessary questions, and do not ask for information that is available in the prospectuses or should have been obtained prior to application. Certainly don't try to brown nose by asking a question about the university's research etc; clearly that can't be answered in your interview and the fact that you think it might demonstrates a distinct lack of realism on your part. Whether you ask a question or not, always thank the interviewer(s) for their time.

A note about clothes

Your personality should be expressed in your answers, not your clothes and accessories. Interviewers are tired and often bored people, so it is easy for them to be distracted, indeed mesmerized, by a piece of bling or interesting hair style. Men; wear a suit and tie. Polish your shoes. Avoid overly styled hair. Ladies, wear a suit or similar. Skirts should not expose your thigh when standing. Remove all but the most subtle jewellery, and tie your hair back. Make up should be subtle.

Suggested timeline of preparation for interview

Two months before the interview

- Don't wait until your interview invitation letter to start preparing.
- Find out when your universities hold their interviews
- Book out these days in your diary.
- Start filling in your skills and qualities chart
- Practice answering some of the common questions
- Get a friend to ask you questions and video your replies
- Watch the video, reflect on your own and your friend's impressions
- Research the university and the course by reading the prospectus, by going on open days and speaking to current students
- Reflect on what you have learnt about medicine during your work experience; what does it mean to you?

When you get your invitation letter

- Reply promptly
- Read the letter closely and get together any supporting documentation that is requested
- Make copies of any certificates

2 weeks before the interview

- Get your interview clothing ready. Put it on and make sure it fits and is appropriate. Get it cleaned.
- Arrange transport, e.g. book train tickets.
- Print out a map of the area that you are travelling to.
- Carry out another practice interview with a friend or colleague, bearing in mind the changes you decided on after your first practice.

Day before the interview

- Prepare your clothes
- Collect certificates and other documentation in a file
- Check time and place of interview again, have a map ready, do not rely on GPS only.
- Check for any traffic/public transport problems (including London underground where applicable).

The day of the interview

- Take a map with you
- Take your invitation letter and contact details.
- Check that you have all the documentation the university requested.
- Arrive at least 30 minutes before the interview time. Be aware that it may take some time to find the right building on a large campus.
- Relax before the interview e.g. by walking around the block.

The interview

- Be friendly and polite with everyone you meet.
- Greet interviewer in a confident, professional, friendly manner.
- Answer questions in a positive tone of voice.
- Have good body language; attentive and formal but relaxed.
- Let your personality come across.

After the interview

- Jot down a few notes about the interview including questions that went well or not so well to help you at your next interview.
- Continue to behave professionally until you are far away from the building.

A Medical Career

UK Modernising Medical Careers (MMC) Specialty Training
Arrows represent a competitive entry process

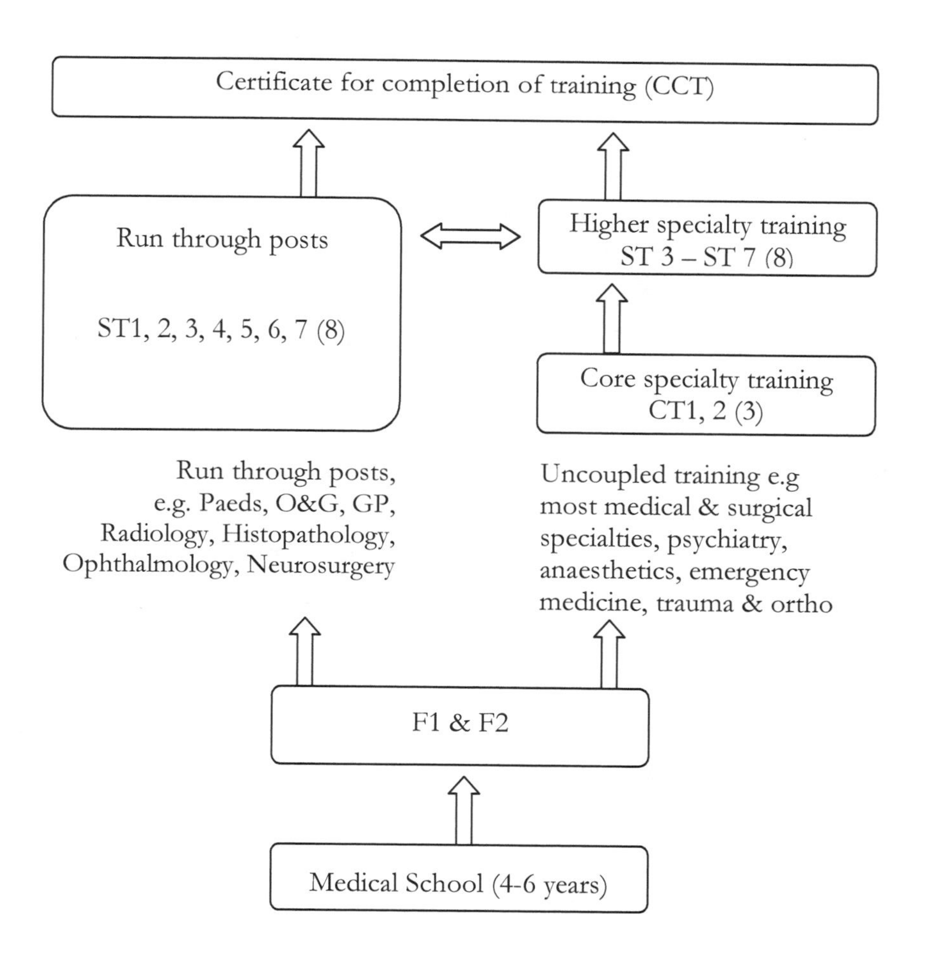

Medical Schools are selecting doctors of the future. It is expected that you know about the career you are applying for (this chapter) and your future employer (next chapter)

In practice, completing the MBBS course is as much a licence to train further as it is a qualification in itself. On the first Wednesday of August following qualification you will begin work as a Foundation year 1 doctor (F1 / FY1). This marks the beginning of junior doctor training, a programme of education and assessment which could lead to a higher training post.

Foundation Programmes

Towards the end of your final year at medical school you will apply for a 'Foundation Programme', a two-year rotation which doctors complete after graduating, before entering into speciality training.

Application to the Foundation Programmes (years 1 and 2) is made via a centralised computer system, similar to UCAS. Postgraduate training is run at a regional level by 'Foundation Schools'. Your application to a Foundation School is made centrally and you will receive one offer only. The Foundation School itself will then allocate you one Foundation Programme. Some Schools accept you onto a 2 year programme, whilst others will only allocate specialties for the first of the two years such that, 6 to 8 months into your first year, you will apply for your second year.

The Foundation programme has replaced the old pre-registration house officer (PRHO) year and is intended to bridge the gap between medical school and specialist or GP training. Information about the programme is available at: *www.foundationprogramme.nhs.uk*

All F1s must work for at least three months (usually four) in medical and surgical specialties, while the remaining months will be spent in another speciality, e.g. microbiology, public health, paediatrics, anaesthetics, intensive care, psychiatry, obstetrics and gynaecology. General practice is not offered until F2.

A typical day as an F1 will consist of some form of 'ward round', during which you review the on-going condition and management of patients who are in hospital under the care of your consultant. This is led by your consultant twice a week, on average, and on other days it is led by the firm's Specialist Trainee or Registrar. The ward round generates jobs for the rest of your day, e.g. ensuring tests and investigations are ordered, performed and reported and referrals to other specialties or centres are made. At the end of each day the F1 updates the list of patients, collates the blood results, generally tidies up any loose ends and informs the on call team of any patients who may be a cause for concern overnight.

Usually at least one day of each week will be the "on take" or "on call" for your team; most patients presenting acutely to the hospital in that time will be admitted under the care of your team. This on take period may last twelve hours (either day or night), twenty four hours, a weekend or in some surgical specialties, a whole week. Although patients admitted during this time will ultimately be under the care of your team, you will not necessarily be at work for the whole time. Twenty four hour on call shifts are a thing of the past, and the maximum allowed nowadays is 13 hours, in line with the European Working Time Directive (EWTD), although in practice this is still not honoured by many trusts. In reality, what is happening, particularly in surgical specialties, is that the 'job' is done in line with EWTD but training e.g. assisting in theatre, is done outside these hours, i.e. unpaid. Towards the end of this chapter you will find an account from a current O&G trainee which highlights the difficulties in this regard.

Other events in your average week may include protected teaching sessions, radiology meetings, multidisciplinary meetings and you may be asked to present interesting cases at departmental meetings. During your surgical job you may be expected to conduct pre-operative assessment clinics where you assess patients' fitness for surgery. Your aim is to highlight any problems which may delay or prevent surgery and organise further investigation or treatment.

Amongst all this, there should be time to enjoy hospital social life and let off steam at the institution (some would say Rite of Passage) that is the Doctors' Mess Party!

Assessment

Your progress through the foundation years will be recorded by you in a Personal Development Portfolio. Much emphasis is placed on assessment and demonstrating competency. These assessments are numerous, take a variety of forms, and require commitment. You will also be expected to reflect on your own practice, the impact of the job on you and on your coping strategies. This ability to reflect on one's practice is frequently tested at medical school interviews.

Foundation Year Two

The second year follows a very similar structure to the F1 year, with four months spent in three different specialties. This year allows you to take more responsibility and to see patients in specialty clinics. You may also be responsible for supervising an F1. There is an emphasis on becoming an "emergency-safe doctor" and many of the available F2 posts include placement in accident and emergency. At the end of F2 you will receive a Foundation Achievement of Competency Document (FACD) and be eligible to apply to specialist training in your chosen field.

The 'Reality' of the Foundation Years.

Hopefully you have shadowed a junior doctor during your work experience and if not, we would recommend that you try to find such an opportunity, so that you can be realistic in your interview about the job for which you are applying.

You will leave medical school with vast medical knowledge, and a healthy ability to communicate, but will be largely deprived of the opportunity to use any of it when you first qualify. Your role may seem to be deemed worthy of less respect than the roles you undertook during your work experience. You may be spoken to badly. You may be bleeped incessantly, whilst you are on the phone, on the computer, talking to patients, talking to relatives, talking to other departments. You may have a list of 60 jobs with only time to do 40 of them, and may struggle to prioritise when everyone else is insisting that their jobs are most important. Pay of less than £30k might seem good at the moment, but it does not rise quickly, and you will have significant debt.

However, even amongst the drudgery of junior days, the job is fascinating, rewarding, fun, and a privilege.

Specialist Training Application

There are two types of training programme in existence: 'run-through training' and 'uncoupled training'. In run-through training (e.g. GP, radiology, paediatrics) you apply competitively to gain a place on the programme and progress through the programme until completion of training, presuming your ongoing performance is satisfactory, both in terms of competency based assessment and in passing the speciality exams. In uncoupled training (e.g. medicine, surgery, anaesthetics), after completion of core training you must re-apply to the specialist training programme.

Training can end in one of two ways; either by moving through the training scheme to achieve a Certificate of Completion of Training (CCT), or GP registration, which entitles doctors to apply for Consultant posts or substantive GP posts respectively; or by choosing to leave training and take up a Career Post, a position referred to as a Staff Grade in the old system. People in these posts are not 'in training' and are employed for service provision.

Run through training is still in its early years and may undergo further reform. However, it is important to realise that run through training forces junior doctors to choose which specialty they wish to pursue at a very early stage in their careers and some may find themselves applying for a specialty of which they have no real experience. It is vital therefore, that you get as broad a base of experience of the various specialties as possible before the time comes to choose.

Postgraduate examinations

For each specialty there is a governing College who is responsible for setting the postgraduate curriculum and examinations and maintaining the standards of training. These exams remain formidable hurdles, even to the seasoned examinee. Passing them earns you the right to become a 'Member' or 'Fellow' of your chosen college. Governing Colleges include:

Royal College of Anaesthetists
Royal College of Emergency Medicine
Royal College of General Practitioners
Royal College of Obstetricians and Gynaecologists
Royal College of Ophthalmologists
Royal College of Pathologists
Royal College of Physicians of the UK
Royal College of Physicians of Edinburgh
Royal College of Psychiatrists
Royal College of Radiologists
Royal College of Surgeons of England
Royal College of Surgeons of Edinburgh
Royal College of Physicians and Surgeons of Glasgow

Appraisal and revalidation

Once you have graduated and completed your foundation training, assessments of various sorts continue. Medicine is a job requiring willingness for life-long learning. As well as examinations to admit you to the various professional bodies above, all doctors in any discipline will also undergo regular appraisal and revalidation whatever their professional level. Essentially, you will be required to provide evidence that you are satisfying the GMC criteria provided in Good Medical Practice.

This is a newly introduced system and so may change over the next few years but at the moment the framework for appraisal is based on four key domains; knowledge, skills and performance; safety and quality; communication, partnership and teamwork; and maintaining trust. Each of these is then subdivided into three main attributes. It will be your responsibility to maintain your e-portfolio to demonstrate that you have satisfied these requirements. Since you will already be using an e-portfolio to manage your learning and personal development, it is not expected that this will increase the burden on doctors but should provide an extra layer of safety for patients.

Academic medicine

A career in academic medicine can be furthered by taking a clinical lectureship position. F1 and F2 academic posts are also available and are open to graduates with a proven record of academic achievement and interest in research, publication and teaching. They incorporate research and clinical practice into the four month placements.

Other medical careers

Hospital doctoring versus general practice is not the only fork in the road for you as you progress; there are other options available to you: public health, forensic medicine, secure environment (prison) medicine and military medicine, as examples.

Representatives of the armed forces will be present at university career days. They can offer financial support during your medical school education in return for a commitment to serve in the armed forces as a commissioned officer, in a medical capacity, for six years following graduation. Your commission can be extended beyond that subject to mutual agreement. There are significant financial benefits as both student and junior doctor. Also experience of medicine in the field is an experience unique to the military personnel. In addition, the forces are very supportive of sporting excellence, giving their trainees time off for these commitments and for 'Adventurous Training Leave'. Of course, military doctors must take up regular postings, often to war zones, to provide a service both to the UK troops and to local civilians.

Useful links

The British Medical Association *www.bma.org.uk*

The NHS homepage for Modernising Medical Careers *www.mmc.nhs.uk*

The General Medical Council *www.gmc-uk.org*

Training and European Working Time Directive

Account from an O&G ST4 trainee

Because of recommendations that obstetrics, as a high risk specialty, should be increasingly consultant led and delivered, expectations are changing. Currently, we have relative job security, as a large number of extra consultants must be trained to deliver this. Also, as a speciality with an increasingly female and less than full time workforce, large numbers of trainees are needed to cover the on-call rota. However, the days of consultants at home overnight and rarely woken, are long gone. Nowadays, consultants tend to work longer hours than juniors, expected to put in a full clinical day either side of a busy night on labour ward. We expect that, in the long term, consultants too will work resident shifts. This will again increase the number required but rewards for long years of training have not been as expected for the current cohort.

EWTD is an ongoing problem, as well as a solution. Yes, it is nice to have some work life balance and doctors do work more efficiently and safely when well rested. Nevertheless, there are implications, such as the loss of consultant firms and continuity in training, not to mention a massive decrease in the time available for training and experience. Salaries have also decreased, as a large proportion used to come from 'unsocial hours' banding. We all used to get band 3, i.e. 100%, which doubled the salary. Now that those hours are illegal (on paper), pay is limited to 50%. In reality, I now earn the same as I did in FY1. With increasing student debt, medicine may no longer equal guaranteed affluence.

The training in obstetrics is always subject to the demands of labour ward, with gynaecology suffering in terms of both service provision and training time in theatre being fiercely competitive. There is a general feeling that the seven years of ST training and holding of a CCT do not adequately prepare a doctor for the responsibility of independent consultant practice. Out of programme experience (OOPE) is, however, difficult to attain as the party line remains that ST should suffice. Particular skills such as ultrasound scanning are often expected to fit into on-call sessions on an ad-hoc basis, which most trainees find unrealistic. There is pressure, therefore, to attain extra skills in unpaid work/training outside contracted hours.

Following the ST trajectory, I myself could CCT at the age of 32 but I find it hard to believe that I would have the skills or confidence to work as a consultant, or that any panel would hire me as one. I also expect that the current comments of, "You're too young/blonde/female to be my doctor," will continue, as patient expectations change slower than our profession. I love my speciality and never considered any other but I am well aware that, without that passion and on paper, it was not necessarily a sound objective choice. But there are moments in obstetrics worth more than any downside.....

Interview Question on Medical Careers

Where do you see yourself in ten years time?

A candidate serious about a career in medicine should be able to fill five minutes talking about their future career.

This question tests your motivation and your realism. Neither is well demonstrated without adequate work experience.

You are likely to fall into one of two groups; 1) someone who has a burning desire to be a doctor but is not sure what sort; or 2) someone who is certain what type of doctor they wish to become. Either is fine, although there are risks with each. You need to flesh out your answer and having too 'flexible' an approach may lead to a rambling answer without clear structure. However, being too certain of anything in medicine is rarely a good idea, and may sound unrealistic.
Either way, you need to give some structure to your answer, with an introduction, a conclusion (or summary) and some content in between. To not use your work experience as part of your answer would be a mistake.

1) For the first group, your answer might commence;
"I have met a number of different types of doctor during my work experience and find myself being drawn to all of their work! I have shadowed GPs, emergency doctors, as well as a surgeon...."
Already you are demonstrating that you have acquired lots of work experience, and more importantly, that you have reflected on it. Or you could start more literally;

"In ten years time I would not yet be a specialist, but I should be on my way to specialising. I would have spent five years at medical school, two years as a foundation year doctor, and of course there is the rest of this year whilst waiting to start medical school. In ten years time I would therefore hope to be

two years into my specialist training, although precisely which area is something I do not yet know."

This answer sounds very realistic, but you would have to be careful not to sound patronising. You will then need to flesh out your answer;

"Different departments have a different appeal for me. I would find GP work very rewarding because...... . During work experience with a GP I found that...... . However during my work experience in A&E I was fascinated by ..."

After telling of your dreams, skills and aspirations, framed in the light of work experience, you would then need to conclude or summarise, for example:

"In summary, there are advantages to different areas of medicine. I hope to be in an area where I gain significant patient contact, in an area which is developing and will remain a challenge to me."

2) For the second group, your answer might commence;

"I have hoped to become a surgeon almost as long as I have wanted to become a doctor! In particular I find gynaecological surgery fascinating and in ten years I hope to be a specialist trainee in Obstetrics and Gynaecology."

This would be a solid introduction reflecting a burning desire. You would need to flesh out this answer describing your motives and your experiences.

"Much of my work experience reflects my interests in surgery, but I have also taken the opportunity to seek out other opportunities. During my O&G shadowing I was struck by the variety of work; young and old, health and illness, and I learnt....."

Your evidence needs to be as much about reflection as it does what you have actually done. Once you have fleshed out your answer, you need to conclude or summarise;

"I recognise that many doctors specialise in areas they did not intend. I realise that my desires may change, and I'm excited about working in other departments during my medical school placements and during foundation years."

These extracts come from realistic and reflective answers which filled five minutes of an MMI station.

The NHS

Whilst there is no requirement to work for the NHS after completion of your medical degree, your interviewers will expect that you will intend to work for the NHS, and will expect you to have some knowledge about your future employer.

You will find lots of very readable information on the NHS website, *www.nhs.uk* and the following is derived from it:

The National Health Service was launched in 1948 and has grown to be the world's largest publicly funded health service. It is also, despite its flaws, one of the most egalitarian. The principle of the NHS is that good healthcare should be available to all, regardless of wealth. With the exception of charges for some prescriptions and optical and dental services, the NHS remains free at the point of use for anyone who is resident in the UK.

The NHS employs more than 1.7m people and around 3 million people are treated in the NHS in England every week.

When the NHS was launched in 1948 it had a budget of £437 million (roughly £9 billion at today's value). For 2011/12 it is around £106 billion. The Department of Health is responsible for the NHS. The Secretary of State for Health

(Jeremy Hunt since September 2012) is the head of the Department of Health and reports to the Prime Minister. The Department of Health controls England's 10 Strategic Health Authorities (SHAs), which oversee all NHS activities in England. In turn, each SHA supervises all the NHS trusts in its area.

The NHS is divided into two sections: primary and secondary care. Primary care is the first point of contact for most people and is delivered by a wide range of independent contractors, including GPs, dentists, pharmacists and optometrists.

Secondary care, or acute healthcare, can be either elective care or emergency care. Elective care means planned specialist medical care or surgery, usually following referral from a primary or community health professional such as a GP.

Primary care trusts (PCTs) are in charge of primary care and have a major role around commissioning secondary care, providing community care services. They are central to the NHS and control 80% of the NHS budget, which is an average of £1,615 per head.

The Changes

There is a lot of information on the Department of Health website *healthandcare.dh.gov.uk* and the following is derived from it:

The Health and Social Care Act 2012 aims are to put clinicians at the centre of commissioning, free up providers to innovate, empower patients and give a new focus to public health.

The suggestion is that the way the system works is changing but there will be no change to the core values of the NHS – health care will remain free at the point of use, funded from taxation, and based on need and not the ability to pay.

Scientific and technological advances mean that we can treat illness more effectively than ever before, but new drugs and treatments are expensive. With better health care, people are living longer. This is an achievement to celebrate, but this trend also means greater pressure on health and care services to maintain people's wellbeing and quality of life for longer. Despite these advances, good health is not shared by all – inequalities persist between communities and regions, with preventable ill health creating significant challenges. We need to get better value from public spending, to invest more in preventing ill health, to enable people to stay in their own homes and to continue to drive improvements in care.

As well as providing patient care, in the new system, doctors, nurses and other professionals will use their knowledge of local health needs to commission the best available services to meet them. They will do this by joining together to form Clinical Commissioning Groups (CCGs). CCGs will have the freedom to commission services for their local community from any service provider which meets NHS standards and costs – these could be NHS hospitals, social enterprises, voluntary organisations or private sector providers.

Local authorities will commission care and support services and have a new responsibility to protect and improve health and wellbeing and will use their knowledge of their communities to tackle challenges such as smoking, alcohol and drug misuse and obesity. A new organization, Public Health England, will provide national leadership and expert services, to support public health and work with local government and the NHS to respond to emergencies.

Most people will need care and support at some point in their lives. Alongside their health care, people need the right combination of care and support – financial, practical and emotional – to manage day-to-day living. Care and health services will be organised to work together to provide seamless services that respond to people's individual needs and choices, including personal budgets to choose the care that is best for them.

NHS services nationally will be supported by the new NHS Commissioning Board (NHS CB). It will fund local CCGs to commission services for their communities and ensure that they do this effectively. Some specialist services will continue to be commissioned by the NHS CB centrally where this is most efficient.

Health trusts will continue to manage hospital care and community and mental health services, with all trusts becoming Foundation Trusts to benefit from greater independence to manage their own services. They will be able to innovate, introducing new approaches to provide the services local CCGs want to commission and they will be able to generate private income to bolster their budgets to the benefit of NHS patients. A new NHS Trust Development Authority will support NHS Trusts to improve so they can take advantage of the benefits of foundation trust status when they are ready.

The National Institute for Health and Clinical Excellence (NICE) will continue to provide guidance on the best care based on the best available evidence. The Care Quality Commission (CQC) will assess the quality and safety of services against government standards through its registration, regulation and monitoring of services, ensuring that people are treated with dignity and respect.

The new health and care system will be up and running by April 2013.

Interview Question about the NHS

Tell me about the NHS

Any candidate serious about a career in medicine should be able to fill five minutes talking about their future employer.

Open questions like this are a good question to separate good from poor candidates. It allows the candidate to develop an answer in line with their knowledge. So a candidate could talk about current structure, or funding, or the history, or the planned changes, or patient views, or all of these things. Of course, an interviewer might ask 'Tell me about the funding of the NHS', although this is a less appropriate question as it is possible that some very good candidates could not answer this.

There are a few general aspects to this question. Firstly, as this is quite an open question, you need to decide (by pausing and thinking) what sort of content you are going to cover. Once you have decided, your answer will benefit from some signposting and structure. Imagine you are writing an essay (indeed, it might be a good idea to do just that in preparation for your interview).

You might start with the NHS 'mission';

"The structure of the NHS is changing; I'd like to tell you about the current structure, and then what will happen next......"(intro and signposting)

This sort of statement provides an introduction and already suggests to the interviewer that you are capable.
And / or;

"The National Health Service was founded in 1948 to provide good health care....."(intro)

You should then be in a position to flesh out your answer either with knowledge, or work experience or even both;

"There are various ways in which the NHS provides healthcare for its patients, such as primary care, secondary care, public

health, emergency care, and the patient journey can start in different places. So for instance a patient with weight loss might present to their GP, whilst a patient who has cut themselves deeply might present to A&E.....(content, knowledge)

"The system is changing, with commissioning care groups being given responsibility for commissioning services for patients. PCTs will no longer exist and.....(content, knowledge)

"I have seen the NHS from different angles during my work experience, and have heard very different attitudes from patients and clinicians. There are some great things about the NHS and some areas which are felt to be less acceptable. I spoke to a number of patients, and those with the most severe illnesses were often more satisfied than those who were using the service at its periphery, for instance.....(content; evidence of work experience)"

If you have neither the knowledge nor the experience to talk for nearly five minutes on this subject of the NHS, you need to put this book down and go and get some.

When you are ready to finish your answer, it can be useful to conclude or summarise, not only for the benefit of your interviewer but also for yourself (interviewees feel very uncomfortable when their answer just tails off with no apparent end, especially when they then have to sit in silence waiting for a buzzer to go. That silent pause feels much better if there has been a good solid end to the answer). Conclusions might include;

"In summary, the NHS is one of the biggest organisations in the world. Making large changes within any organisation is tough, but for the NHS is an even bigger task. Whilst these changes will hopefully be complete by the time I qualify, I believe I have the ability to deal with changes in the future, to keep up to date, and to be an asset to the NHS in whatever form."

"In summary, there are many different aspects to the NHS, and I have been privileged enough to see some of them in action. Each department works in different ways, and differently for each patient, but always with the same common goal."

"In summary, whilst there are many negative opinions of the NHS, I believe it to be something for which our country should be proud. There is no perfect health service, any more than there is perfect health, but the NHS seems to get it about right most of the time for most people."

Remember though, that we cannot predict precisely what question you will get, and you cannot, and should not, pre-prepare answers to everything and anything you might be asked in this subject area. You need three things to answer any question in this area:

1) Knowledge
2) Work Experience
3) A thoughtful, reflective and structured approach.

Work Experience

"Before I had even applied to medicine I gained various different work experiences. I volunteered at a hospital, and at the social club of a psychiatric hospital, worked at a school for young people with severe autistic spectrum disorders, shadowed a GP and also a hepatology team in a hospital. I think that this wide range of experience helped my application enormously. However, I also worked as a Nursing Assistant and this is definitely, by a long, long stretch, the best experience I have gained. I actually now think that nobody should apply to medicine without having worked as a Nursing Assistant/HCA; it is just invaluable, mainly because it gives the most realistic view of working in a hospital, actually gets you involved in working in health care, is insanely interesting (and confirming that one does indeed want to be a doctor) and gives you masses to talk about at interview. My other experiences were useful for my personal statement and interviews, but talking about working in the hospital seemed crucial."

Successful Medical School Applicant

Work experience defines a good candidate. For many medical students it represents a journey of self-discovery; a transition from idealism to reality. There is no substitute for tangible experience in a healthcare setting where candidates can examine what it means to be a health professional. Medical schools give much weight to work experience at interview. Just doing work experience is little in itself; at interview you will impress not for what you did, but rather what it did to you.

Quality and quantity are important - it can be of the highest standard, but if you only gained two weekends of experience in the past year, your commitment to truly dedicating yourself to medicine may be in question. Work experience is not a token gesture, or a box to be ticked. It is vital to your hopes and aspirations. To be able to present yourself as a potential doctor, you have to have some awareness of what it is to actually *be* a doctor. This is borne out of work experience which has been reflected on, and which resonates with you in your application.

Useful types of work experience

The gold standard is hands-on work in a caring role in a hospital or nursing home, although this is not possible for everyone. However, it is vital that you get the chance to spend time with elderly, sick or disabled people who may be frustrated or confused, vulnerable and in need of help; i.e. exactly what you will have to deal with as a junior doctor.

- Do you have some of the same skills as a good doctor?
- Can you relate to the way good doctors conduct themselves?
- What do good doctors do well?
- Have you seen a poor doctor? What made him sub-optimal?

All of these questions can be answered without reference to work experience – by anyone – so you must use your own unique work experience to make your answer relevant and insightful. You will have thoughts on these issues already, but they will become far more profound when framed in the context of hands-on work experience.

If experience developed your awareness of the responsibilities, challenges, trials and tribulations of what of means to be a clinician, you're clearly going to benefit greatly. There are many opportunities through which you will be able to gain real insight.

Care Work

- Care work e.g. care assistant at residential home/ care home for the elderly/disabled/ residential home for children with e.g. autism
- Volunteer at hospital/ volunteer auxiliary/ ward volunteer
- Volunteer at a soup kitchen, centre for the homeless
- Mentoring and tutoring
- Volunteer counselling
- Befriending services to disadvantaged/ elderly
- Community work

These are simply some ideas to hopefully spark your own imagination, or nudge you in a useful direction.

Shadowing

Although shadowing rarely affords any hands-on exposure, it is important that you shadow a doctor. Shadowing does not replace care work or similar, but provides a valuable adjunct opportunity. You can also learn a great deal by shadowing other healthcare professionals. For instance, if you shadow a GP, try to also observe the community nurses or midwives. Many candidates get very excited about the prospect of spending time with, say, a top consultant neurosurgeon. You would not turn down this opportunity, as it is a wonderful one, but remember the limitations of what it tells you about an average patient's needs and an average doctor's workload.

Other useful experiences through hobbies

You may be able to additionally demonstrate transferable skills through experiences not directly related to medicine. For instance, those candidates who play sport may find that there are some very rewarding opportunities allied to their sport with e.g. the disabled.

Experiences for candidates already working in a healthcare setting

If you are currently a pharmacist, PhD student, NHS manager, social worker or any other professional involved with patients, healthcare or research, you will clearly have extensive insight into your particular field. However, your role could be narrow, and also biased. Gaining hands-on care experience is important. Aside from improving your insight, you will be able to more easily demonstrate yourself to be a well-rounded, interested and motivated individual.

Reading

Although not strictly work experience, it is useful to mention again the notion of reading widely. In much the same way as your medical knowledge develops at medical school, your understanding of current affairs and advancements in medicine will be superior if built over time. Read widely, and maintain objectivity by always considering the different impacts on all parties affected by any article that you read. Indeed, when reading a newspaper article on a recent development consider what it means to patients. Use your work experience to ask patients what the latest stories mean to them.

Personal experiences

Your insight into medicine through your own personal experience as a relative or carer may be very useful. If these experiences form a large part of your desire to become a doctor, it may be worth taking the time to think about your unique situation from other people's point of view and to try, in so far as it's possible, to put the experience into more objective and general terms. Taking time to reflect and articulate on these experiences prior to interview can be very useful.

How do I make it tangible? - getting the most out of your work experience

Satisfactory demonstration of attributes such as empathy, intellectual ability, ability to accept responsibility and handle stress, communication, teamwork and so on is dependent on your analysis, criticism and insight into that experience.

During your chosen experiences, you should try to seize the opportunity to gain an understanding in as many aspects of healthcare as you can:

- Be able to recognise and empathise with the needs of patients
- Communicate with patients and the medical staff
- Recognise what makes a good doctor

- Recognise the skills that *you* have that reflect those of a good doctor
- Seize any opportunities to develop those skills
- Recognise the importance of the multi-disciplinary team
- Consider the problems facing patients, relatives, doctors and other healthcare professionals
- Consider your own prejudices, fears and concerns

This is by no means an exhaustive list of issues that you might dwell on during your work experience. Indeed, a list somewhat detracts from the preferred notion that you gain an understanding that is an intricately woven ensemble of practicalities, emotions, finances, ethics and management issues.

For all of the skills mentioned throughout this book and elsewhere, try to witness and achieve them during your work experience. Empathise with patients. Talk to them, listen to their needs. Ask them about their care. Be kind. Be thoughtful. Be responsible. Talk to doctors. Talk to other healthcare professionals. Empathise with them too.

- What do doctors love about their job?
- Is it all they had hoped?
- What are the problems facing doctors, other healthcare professionals, patients and their relatives?
- How do you feel about financial constraints?
- How do you feel about sickness, suffering and death?
- How do you feel about bodily fluids, unsightly conditions and nasty smells?

Keep a Diary

The key use of your diary should be to reflect upon memorable moments and interesting patients, your own emotions, and things you have witnessed. When you prepare for interview, this collection of ideas and emotions will be of enormous help to you in relating your thoughts in a fresh and dynamic way.

For each of the situations that you note in your diary, also try to empathise with those involved.

- How do the doctors behave?
- What cheered a patient most?
- Do you have a most memorable patient experience?
- Why did another behave aggressively?
- Are some patients frightened?
- Do they understand their diagnosis and treatment?
- What side effects does their medication have on them?

You may find that by communicating and empathising with patients, you may not only be better able to answer these questions, you might also provide a great deal of support to a patient in need when other healthcare professionals simply cannot afford the time. Also try to think realistically about how you would feel if you were caring for such a patient in addition to many others. Take advantage of opportunities, for instance; if you witness a practical procedure, take the time to go back and talk to the patient about how it was for them.

Similarly, when you see a good doctor in action, think about every facet of why that doctor was good.

- What was a good doctor's body language like?

- What questions did they ask?
- Did they listen and really pick up on the patient's underlying message?
- What information did they give? How did they give it?
- Have you asked patients what they think makes a good doctor?
- Do you have these qualities?
- Can you demonstrate them?
- Can you improve on them?

Be careful not to be a maverick and focus on the flaws of the system (for you will see many). Of course it can be easier and sometimes more natural to exemplify skills by considering the consequences of their absence. It is important to recognise inadequacies; they exist and one needs to be realistic. However, remember that, on balance, you should *want* to work within the NHS with patients and health care professionals, rather than feel that it is something you could simply *cope* with.

Candidates (well, those without relevant experience) invariably moan about how difficult it is to get work experience. It can be obtained with time and perseverance, motivation and a positive outlook, and excusing yourself from the task will not be received positively. Once gained it will stand you in good stead; but only if it was meaningful and you took time for reflection.

MMI work experience question

How has your work experience confirmed your desire to become a doctor?

This question is very personal and requires honesty and reflection. I applied to medicine over a decade ago, but was asked a question very similar to this. One of my interviewers was later a mentor and recalled my answer as being excellent. It went something along the lines of:

"I have shadowed doctors, worked in care homes, and have experience of research, all of which has furthered my desire to study medicine. However, the most profound experience in terms of confirming my desire to be a doctor was an experience at a care home for autistic children.

"I work at the home at the weekends, helping them in the office in the mornings and more direct care work in the afternoons. I have found it very rewarding to be able to care for the children. None of them had any conventional language skills, but were often able to communicate in other ways. It was also rewarding to be able to communicate with parents, who experienced many, often conflicting, emotions. However, the most profound experience happened whilst I was looking after a group of five children, aged between about eight and twelve years. One of them appeared to be scratching her lower back when suddenly she threw a handful of her own faeces across the room. It landed on my upper chest and shoulder. I called for help to look after the other children, then took the little girl to the bathroom, bathed her, cleaned myself, and went back with her to my post.

I was organised, calm and thought about all the children and not just the one who was soiled.

"I would always have hoped that I would behave in this way but really couldn't have been sure as I'm an excitable type of person. Therefore, my emotional response at the time was a revelation, even if that sounds a bit dramatic. I did not have even the slightest sense of stress, anxiety, anger, or any other negative emotion. I never would have known how calm I would be in this sort of situation until this happened. It seems that my caring attitude and professionalism are already well honed, and I realised then, and later on more reflection, that medicine was exactly the right path for me. From that moment, I have felt a deep confidence that I might one day make a wonderful doctor."

Every word of this story is true; it is precisely the point at which my desire to become a doctor became a certainty. As an often intense person, I would not have expected to react so calmly. This work experience was not just a useful story at interview, it was enormously important in my certainty that becoming a doctor was right for me.

There is an inherent structure to the story. Whilst I did not know I was doing it at the time, I was employing the 'STARR' structure for answering questions, which stands for:

Situation or **T**ask
Action and
Results and
Reflection.

In a question where you can use your work experience, the STARR approach might be useful.

Ultimately, it was the honesty and realism of this story, both in terms of what happened and what I learnt from it, which my interviewer found so excellent.

Summary

- Work experience is necessary for you to make an informed decision, for your personal statement, and to compete at interview.
- Care work is the gold standard to see the humble side of medicine.
- Shadowing is necessary; and a junior doctor may give you more insight than a senior doctor.
- Start looking early. There's plenty out there, but it takes time.
- You must learn from your work experience. Keep a reflective diary.
- Talk to patients, doctors and other staff. Read about relevant aspects of their care and illness in the national press, textbooks and journals.

The Personal Statement

Not all schools use personal statements at interview, but you are likely to be applying to at least one school that does. Even for the few schools who will not use your UCAS statement, your interviewers are likely to explore at least some, if not all, of the type of qualities that might be included in your statement:

- Convincing explanation of the candidate's desire
- Commitment to a career in medicine
- Intellectual and academic strength
- An empathic attitude
- Non-academic achievements
- Realistic attitude about the profession and course
- Self-motivation
- Good organisational skills
- Growth as a person
- A 'well rounded' personality
- Demonstration of a wide range of interests
- Awareness of current developments

You should be able to explain, develop, defend and reflect upon everything and anything in your personal statement. If you have embellished the truth in your personal statement, you have shown a lack of probity and if caught, will fail. For instance, stating that you understand something that you have little awareness of, stating that you regularly read a journal when you do not know what was in the last issue, or stating that you have become aware of end of life issues but have no knowledge to back this up. Clearly, downright lying about something you have done is a swift route to rejection. Similarly, be cautious if you are considering including future work experience plans in your statement, because if these plans are not realised, then you will be left in the uncomfortable position of having to explain why.

A single MMI station lends itself perfectly to asking specific questions from the candidate's statement. Here are some personal statements followed by the sort of questions which might arise from it.

Statement One

The author of this statement was invited to interview at all four medical schools to which he applied.

I believe working within the NHS will be one of the most rewarding aspects of being a doctor, supporting a healthcare system in which anyone, regardless of circumstance, is entitled to medical treatment. Through work experience, voluntary care work and continued academic study, my desire to become a doctor has intensified. Although medicine can be a tough and stressful career, I look forward to the many challenges it will bring both intellectually and emotionally. My strong desire to care for others whilst furthering my keen interest in science has made me certain that medicine is a career I am determined to devote my life to.
I arranged five days at the Royal Berks Hospital, which included observing a consultant anaesthetist, arthroplasty shoulder surgery and the ICU. Although the surgical procedures fascinated me, I was more amazed by the number of staff needed to keep the theatres running. It really helped me to understand the crucial role of teamwork and communication in a multidisciplinary environment. Accompanying a junior doctor on presurgical visits to patients gave me a valuable insight into the role of junior doctors. To expand my

experience of primary care, I organised a week at a GP surgery. I sat in on consultations, went on home visits and observed the practice nurse. It was incredible to see the complex skill of diagnosis and it gave me an awareness of the huge workload and difficult time constraints on GPs.

My regular work looking after a baby has furthered my understanding of the great trust put in carers and my awareness of how challenging but satisfying caring can be. Since December 2009, I have also been working as a weekly voluntary healthcare assistant at a local care home. It has been very rewarding to develop a relationship with some of the residents, such as one gentleman, who has dementia. It was gratifying to comfort him when he was anxious and to talk about his planned cataract surgery. These experiences continue to strengthen my interpersonal and communication skills and it has been fascinating to see a neurological condition that links to my biology study of the nervous system. Dementia is a subject I am keen to research more deeply.

Whilst I was a peer mentor, my ability to encourage and empathise with the younger students was vital and it was rewarding to see them progress. As the student organiser of the Henley Youth Festival, I collaborated with youth workers to involve young people from the whole community. This was a good experience of working in a team under pressure. As a doctor, it will be vital for me to be able to pass on skills and knowledge to others. My presentation and communication skills have developed in my role as student ambassador at my college and I am further strengthening these abilities as a children's music teacher.

Academic achievement is important to me and I have been awarded school prizes, UK Maths Challenge Gold Award and The Lions Club music prize. However, to combat stress, I believe it is crucial to find the right balance between work and leisure. I regularly play tennis at my local club and at school I was a member of the Rugby and Athletics squads. I play in my college jazz band and have also encouraged friends to form a rock band, for which I compose, play guitar and sing. Performing at music events has greatly increased my confidence, especially when speaking and singing to large audiences. I am studying for my grade 8 classical guitar, which I am determined to complete shortly.

I am convinced I have the ambition and qualities needed to succeed in medicine and would relish the opportunity to work within a professional team to help make a difference to people's lives. The freedom given at my college has required me to be self-motivated and determined to succeed which makes me confident that I am well prepared for independent study. I look forward to actively taking part in university life and am excited by the prospect of life-long learning.

Questions which could arise from this statement

Paragraph One:

I believe working within the ***NHS*** will be one of the most rewarding aspects of being a doctor, supporting a healthcare system in which anyone, regardless of circumstance, is entitled to medical treatment. Through work experience, voluntary care work and continued academic study, my desire to become a doctor has intensified. Although medicine can be a ***tough and stressful*** career, I look forward to the many ***challenges*** it will bring both ***intellectually and emotionally***. My strong desire to care for others whilst furthering my keen ***interest in science*** has made me certain that medicine is a career I am determined to devote my life to.

- Tell me about the NHS.
- Tell me how medicine can be tough and stressful.
- Give me an example of an intellectual challenge faced by one of the doctors during your work experience.
- Give me an example of an emotional challenge faced by one of the doctors during your work experience.
- Tell me something that fascinates you in science.

Paragraph Two:

I arranged five days at the Royal Berks Hospital, which included observing a consultant ***anaesthetist***, ***arthroplasty*** shoulder surgery and the ICU. Although the surgical procedures fascinated me, I was more amazed by the ***number of staff needed*** to keep the theatres running. It really helped me to ***understand the*** crucial role of teamwork and communication in a ***multidisciplinary*** environment. Accompanying a junior doctor on ***presurgical*** visits to patients gave me a valuable insight into the ***role of junior doctors***. To expand my experience of primary care, I organised a week at a GP surgery. I sat in on consultations, went on ***home visits*** and observed the ***practice nurse***. It was incredible to see the complex skill of diagnosis and it gave me an awareness of the huge workload and difficult time ***constraints*** on GPs.

- Tell me what anaesthetists do. (The candidate should know that their role extends beyond anaesthesia.)
- I am a patient about to undergo an arthroplasty; please explain the procedure to me. (This question tests the candidate's knowledge, but more importantly, it tests the candidate's ability to describe things in lay terms.)
- Tell me about the roles of the people running an operating theatre.
- Give me another example of a multidisciplinary team.
- Talk me through the things the junior doctor did in presurgical assessments.
- Tell me about the rest of the role of a junior doctor.
- Tell me about some home visits you attended with the GP.
- Tell me about the work of the practice nurse.
- Tell me about the time constraints faced by GPs.

Paragraph Three:
My regular work ***looking after a baby*** has furthered my understanding of the great trust put in carers and my awareness of how ***challenging*** but satisfying caring can be. Since December 2009, I have also been working as a weekly voluntary healthcare assistant at a local care home. It has been very rewarding to develop a relationship with some of the residents, such as one gentleman, who has ***dementia***. It was gratifying to comfort him when he was anxious and to talk about his planned ***cataract surgery***. These experiences continue to strengthen my interpersonal and communication skills and it has been fascinating to see a neurological condition that links to my biology study of the nervous system. Dementia is a subject I am keen to research more deeply.

- Please tell me more about your work looking after a baby.
- Tell me about the challenges facing carers.

- Tell me about dementia. (It is hoped that the candidate will describe dementia in terms of both biology and in terms of patients.)
- Did any of the patients with whom you developed a relationship pass away? How did you feel about it?
- Should a care home patient with dementia be offered cataract surgery? (This is an ethical dilemma, as there are two sides to this question. On the one hand, the GMC's '*Good Medical Practice*' (and hopefully, the candidate's conscience) states that one should not let our views or prejudices, including those regarding age and disability, influence the treatment we offer. However, the NHS resources are limited, and access to cataract operations is, in many areas of the country, also limited. Decisions should be based on cost vs benefit, or more broadly, risk vs benefit.)

Paragraph Four:
Whilst I was a ***peer mentor***, my ability to encourage and empathise with the younger students was vital and it was rewarding to see them progress. As the student organiser of the Henley Youth Festival, I collaborated with youth workers to involve young people from the whole community. This was a good experience of working in a ***team under pressure***. As a doctor, it will be vital for me to be able to pass on skills and knowledge to others. My presentation and communication skills have developed in my role as student ambassador at my college and I am further strengthening these abilities as a children's music teacher.

- Tell us about your role and responsibilities as a peer mentor.
- Tell me about the team pressures when you worked on the Youth Festival.

Paragraphs Five and Six:
Academic achievement is important to me and I have been awarded school prizes, UK Maths Challenge Gold Award and The Lions Club music prize. However, to combat stress, I believe it is crucial to find the right balance between work and leisure. I regularly play ***tennis*** at my local club and at school I was a member of the Rugby and Athletics squads. I play in my college jazz band and have also encouraged friends to form a rock band, for which I compose, play guitar and sing. Performing at music events has greatly increased my confidence, especially when speaking and singing to large audiences. I am studying for my grade 8 classical guitar, which I am ***determined to complete shortly***.
I am convinced I have the ambition and qualities needed to succeed in medicine and would relish the opportunity to work within a professional team to help make a difference to people's lives. The freedom given at my college has required me to be self-motivated and determined to succeed which makes me confident that I am well prepared for independent study. I look forward to actively ***taking part in university life*** and am excited by the prospect of life-long learning.

- Describe the rules of tennis to me.
- Have you completed your grade 8 classical guitar?
- Which of your extra-curricular activities do you hope to maintain at medical school? Do you know anything about the societies for these activities at this university?
- How do you balance your workload with these different activities? What would you do if at some stage you felt that you did not have time to give work the attention it deserved? (There is clearly a right answer here, in that work must come first, but how that is achieved should be discussed. Maintaining hobbies and interests maintains health, which in turn keeps people fit to do a good job. It would be a weak answer to simply say that one would give up hobbies if there was no time.)

Statement Two

The author of this statement was invited to interview at all four of the medical schools to which she applied.

A doctor is much more than an expert in Biology; rather a rounded human-being with a balance of proficiency, knowledge and excellent people skills. I believe I have these skills, coupled with a real hunger for knowledge and the desire to commit myself to the lifelong study of a subject that fascinates me.

Having undertaken extensive work experience, I understand the rigours of Medicine and have seen the profession from many angles. Starting in 2006, I volunteered every Saturday for a year at Epsom Hospital with the League of Friends, delivering newspapers and speaking to elderly patients with few visitors. Although I found some situations saddening, I saw that compassion and a kind gesture could make a marked improvement to someone's day-to-day life. I believe that communication and sensitivity are as much a part of being a doctor as clinical competence.

A week in a Radiography Department in 2007 gave me an insight into the practical demands of hospital life. I felt at home and found it a fascinating environment, witnessing how imaging could be used in minor procedures and diagnostics. I relished feeling part of such a strong team, with each member pooling their specialised knowledge to diagnose the patient.

I feel my numerous hobbies have equipped me with essential teamwork skills. I have a love of sport and have played in various successful netball teams, where it is crucial that each person pulls their weight and understands each other's moves. I believe a strong Doctor must be independent and decisive, but also able to step back when required and be a reliable team member.

I also have a passion for music, which involves teamwork, but also independent study skills and perseverance. I have been a committed member of numerous musical ensembles, play the piano and 'cello to Grade 7 and taught myself the flute and saxophone to Grade 5 so that I could play in a Big Band. I enjoy acquiring new skills and gain satisfaction from achieving challenges I set myself. This also proves my ability to acquire new skills quickly and independently.

I have demonstrated my academic ability by achieving 11A*s for GCSE and 3 As at A level. Biology has always been one of my favourite subjects; I find the complexity and ingenuity of body systems and how they work in synchrony truly awe-inspiring. Medicine excites me because it is the opportunity to not only gain copious knowledge of these systems, but to learn how they can be tweaked so that the life that they sustain is as fulfilling as it can be. I have a well-rounded academic interest, with my GCSEs ranging from Art to Statistics. At A

level I discovered a passion for English Literature, for which I was awarded the Year Prize in year 11 and 13 and was also elected English prefect. In this role, I ran a creative writing club, improving my communication skills. I understand and am excited by the fact that a career in Medicine is a lifelong learning curve.
Attending a 3-day 'Medlink' course gave me a unique opportunity to see what a career in Medicine entails from the professionals. I found one exercise particularly interesting; a role-play where we had to ask a patient sensitively about their symptoms and provide a diagnosis. Not only did I see the importance of tact, but competence in problem-solving, which is something I really enjoy and excel at. Whilst at school, I obtained Gold and Bronze certificates in the logic-based UK Maths Challenge. My study of Maths to A-level has also developed my ability to view and attack concepts from different angles. Another problem-solving challenge I enjoyed was an Enterprise programme, where I won the overall prize for my invention idea. The development process involved identifying obstacles and finding solutions, a process mirrored in Medicine.
I have a keen interest in medical ethics and my work with 'Disability Challengers' and assisting with the disabled sport 'Boccia' in the last year has opened my eyes to the struggle of living with disability and the invaluable work of doctors. The clear enjoyment children gain from the activities is hugely rewarding for me and proved that Medicine has done both them and society a huge favour by improving the quality of, and ultimately sustaining, their lives. I can think of nothing I would rather be a part of. As doctors have to relate to all ages, 18 months of voluntary work with Brownies starting n 2006, was also a hugely valuable experience.
Medicine excites me because it is diverse, rewarding and continually develops in unpredictable directions. I have made an informed decision that Medicine is for me, as I am aware that it can, at times, be emotionally, academically and physically demanding. But I feel that I have proved I have the skills, commitment and drive to make a valuable contribution to Medicine.

Questions which could arise from this statement

Paragraphs One and Two:

A doctor is much more than an expert in Biology; rather a rounded human-being with a balance of proficiency, knowledge and excellent people skills. I believe I have these skills, coupled with a real hunger for knowledge and the desire to commit myself to the lifelong study of a subject that ***fascinates*** me.
Having undertaken extensive work experience, I understand the rigours of Medicine and have seen the profession from many angles. Starting in 2006, I volunteered every Saturday for

a year at Epsom Hospital with the ***League of Friends***, delivering newspapers and speaking to ***elderly patients*** with few visitors. Although I found some situations ***saddening***, I saw that compassion and a kind gesture could make a marked improvement to someone's day-to-day life. I believe that communication and sensitivity are as much a part of being a doctor as clinical competence.

- Tell me something about medicine which fascinates you. (This answer requires a degree of knowledge and expertise.)
- What is the League of Friends at Epsom Hospital?
- What did you learn from elderly patients?
- Please can you tell me about a situation that saddened you.

Paragraph Three:
A week in a ***Radiography*** Department in 2007 gave me an insight into the practical demands of hospital life. I felt at home and found it a fascinating environment, witnessing how ***imaging*** could be used in minor ***procedures*** and diagnostics. I relished feeling part of such a strong team, with each member pooling their specialised knowledge to diagnose the patient.

- Tell me how a radiographer differs from a radiologist.
- Describe different types of imaging.
- When were different types of imaging invented? (This sort of question might throw a candidate as it is unlikely that they will know exact dates, but it would be expected that they have some understanding that X-rays have been used for over a hundred years, whilst MRI is much more recent, for instance.)
- Tell me about an interventional radiology procedure that you saw.
- Now that radiographs are digital, should they be reported overseas so that NHS costs are reduced?

Paragraph Five:

I have demonstrated my academic ability by achieving 11A*s for GCSE and 3 As at A level. Biology has always been one of my favourite subjects; I find the complexity and ingenuity of body systems and how they work in synchrony truly awe-inspiring. Medicine excites me because it is the opportunity to not only gain copious knowledge of these systems, but to learn how they can be tweaked so that the life that they sustain is as fulfilling as it can be. I have a well-rounded academic interest, with my GCSEs ranging from ***Art*** to Statistics. At A level I discovered a passion for ***English Literature***, for which I was awarded the Year Prize in year 11 and 13 and was also elected ***English prefect***. In this role, I ran a creative writing club, improving my communication skills. I understand and am excited by the fact that a career in Medicine is a lifelong learning curve.

- Why do you find it useful to have studied Art at GCSE?
- Tell me about the Bronte Sisters.
- Tell me about your role as English prefect.

Paragraph Six:
Attending a 3-day '***Medlink***' course gave me a unique opportunity to see what a career in Medicine entails from the professionals. I found one exercise particularly interesting; a ***role-play*** where we had to ask a patient sensitively about their symptoms and provide a ***diagnosis***. Not only did I see the importance of tact, but competence in problem-solving, which is something I really enjoy and excel at. Whilst at school, I obtained Gold and Bronze certificates in the logic-based UK ***Maths*** Challenge. My study of Maths to A-level has also developed my ability to view and attack concepts from different angles. Another problem-solving challenge I enjoyed was an ***Enterprise*** programme, where I won the overall prize for my invention idea. The development process involved identifying obstacles and finding solutions, a process mirrored in Medicine.

- What did you learn at the Medlink course?
- What was the diagnosis in the role play? (The interviewer could then repeat the role play)

- Describe Pythagoras' theorem to me.
- What was your invention idea?

Paragraph Seven:
I have a keen interest in ***medical ethics*** and my work with 'Disability Challengers' and assisting with the disabled sport '***Boccia***' in the last year has opened my eyes to the struggle of living with disability and the invaluable ***work of doctors***. The clear enjoyment children gain from the activities is hugely rewarding for me and proved that Medicine has done both them and society a huge favour by improving the quality of, and ultimately sustaining, their lives. I can think of nothing I would rather be a part of. As doctors have to relate to all ages, 18 months of voluntary work with ***Brownies*** starting in 2006, was also a hugely valuable experience.

- Tell me the four main ethical principles.
- What is Boccia?
- How can doctors help people who have significant motor skill deficiencies?
- Tell me about your work with the Brownies.

Paragraph Eight:
Medicine excites me because it is diverse, rewarding and continually develops in unpredictable directions. I have made an informed decision that Medicine is for me, as I am aware that it can, at times, be emotionally, academically and ***physically demanding***. But I feel that I have proved I have the skills, commitment and drive to make a valuable contribution to Medicine.

- Tell me why being a doctor can be physically demanding.

Statement Three

The graduate author of this statement was invited to interview at three of the medical schools to which she applied.

My decision to pursue a career in medicine has been a gradual one. Whilst reading a degree in English Literature has broadened my analytical skills, studying A-level Biology simultaneously has enhanced my inclination towards a scientific career for which I now have resolute determination. I am making this application with a degree of commitment and maturity I couldn't have possessed three years ago. It was a job in a pharmacy that ignited my interest in medicine and ever since I have continued to seek experience in health care to ensure my decision is the right one.

Whilst on holiday from university I work for Bluebird Care as a care worker for the elderly and disabled. The job entails independent home visits where I deliver personal care, assist with mobility, and help administer medication. I find being that being a part of the team is rewarding and satisfying but it also demands commitment and professionalism. Often those I work with struggle to deal with their diagnosis both physically and mentally which can be emotionally challenging. Here I see a side of medicine that is unglamorous and distressing. I have nurtured an understanding that, despite a discouraging prognosis, there is always something that can be done to improve a patient's welfare. Daily I witness how people cope with conditions such as multiple sclerosis, dementia and the consequences of stroke. I have acquired a particular interest in Parkinson's disease; and have developed an understanding of its symptoms so that I can deliver the utmost support to those I care for. This experience has strengthened my desire for a dynamic career centred upon scientific knowledge which can be applied whilst interacting with people on a daily basis.

Performing an administrative role at The Falkland Surgery allowed me an extensive insight into the workings of a general practice. I witnessed how GPs coordinate chronic disease management, effective family planning and the treatment of acute infections. I marked how commonly they dealt with the diagnosing of depression. The Lancet article "Clinical diagnosis of depression in primary care: a meta-analysis" further stimulated my interest in this area.

During my gap year I worked as a live-in Matron at Eagle House Prep School. Spending nights on call, I became accustomed to helping unwell children in the middle of the night. Communicating with concerned parents was a fundamental part of the role and consequentially I built upon my decision making skills and developed a matured knowledge of my limitations.

I gained work experience at Frimley Park Hospital where I shadowed a

consultant orthopaedic surgeon and a junior doctor. I had the opportunity to witness surgical procedures such as a dynamic hip screw and the reduction of a displaced radius fracture. I was also able to observe care delivered outside theatre in the form of ward rounds, fracture clinics and morning trauma briefings. During time spent with a junior doctor I cultivated an understanding of the NHS medical training system and the workings of a multidisciplinary team. Furthermore I accumulated a realistic appreciation of the challenges associated with a medical career. My experience demonstrated to me the necessary motivation and commitment required to withstand such trials.
Whilst I consistently seek academic success and find it a rewarding objective I enjoy creative and physical activities in which I partake regularly. I play for my university hockey club and for the last three years have coached sports and drama on a three week summer camp, ISCA, for American middle school children. My position as a camp councillor requires a combination of effective communication, physical stamina and leadership skills, all are qualities which I aspire to carry with me through a career in medicine.

Questions which could arise from this statement

Paragraph One:

My decision to pursue a career in medicine has been a gradual one. Whilst reading a degree in ***English Literature*** has broadened my ***analytical skills***, studying A-level ***Biology*** simultaneously has enhanced my inclination towards a scientific career for which I now have resolute determination. I am making this application with a degree of commitment and maturity I couldn't have possessed three years ago. It was a job in a ***pharmacy*** that ignited my interest in medicine and ever since I have continued to seek experience in health care to ensure my decision is the right one.

- What did you gain from your degree in English Literature?
- How has it broadened your analytical skills?
- What is the most interesting thing you learnt in A-level Biology?
- What was your role in the pharmacy?
- Tell me about the role of a pharmacist.

Paragraph Two:
Whilst on holiday from university I work for Bluebird Care as a care worker for the elderly and disabled. The job entails independent home visits where I deliver personal care, assist with ***mobility***, and help administer medication. I find being that being a part of the team is rewarding and ***satisfying*** but it also demands commitment and professionalism. Often those I work with struggle to deal with their diagnosis both physically and mentally which can be ***emotionally challenging***. Here I see a side of medicine that is unglamorous and distressing. I have nurtured an understanding that, despite a discouraging prognosis, there is always something that can be done to improve a patient's welfare. Daily I witness how people cope with conditions such as multiple sclerosis, dementia and the consequences of stroke. I have acquired a particular interest in ***Parkinson's disease***; and have developed an understanding of its symptoms so that I can deliver the utmost support to those I care for. This experience has strengthened my desire for a dynamic career centred upon scientific knowledge which can be applied whilst interacting with people on a daily basis.

- What training have you had to assist with mobility?
- What is most satisfying about the job?
- Describe a time when you have felt emotionally challenged in this role.
- Have you ever felt out of your depth in this role? (This is a test not so much of ability to do the job, but the vital skill of being able to recognise ones limitations.)
- Tell me about Parkinson's disease. (Here we would be looking for an understanding of both the science and the impact on patients.)
- Many patients in this type of group are admitted to hospital to die, when most would prefer to remain at home. Why do you think this happens and what could be done about it? (This is an MMI station in its own right, and will be looked at later.)

Paragraph Three:
Performing an administrative role at The Falkland Surgery allowed me an extensive insight into the ***workings of a general practice***. I witnessed how GPs coordinate chronic disease management, effective family planning and the treatment of acute infections. I marked how commonly they dealt with the diagnosing of depression. The ***Lancet article*** "Clinical diagnosis of depression in primary care: a meta-analysis" ***further stimulated my interest*** in this area.

- Tell me about the roles of different staff in a GP surgery.
- Tell me about the Lancet article.
- What else have you read about depression?
- What would you do if you thought that a colleague was depressed?

Paragraph Four:
During my gap year I worked as a live-in Matron at Eagle House Prep School. Spending nights on call, I became accustomed to helping ***unwell children in the middle of the night***. Communicating with concerned parents was a fundamental part of the role and consequentially I built upon my decision making skills and developed a matured knowledge of my limitations.

- How did you decide whether to involve a doctor or the parents when a child was sick?
- How did you deal with difficult parents? (As well as describing techniques for dealing with difficult parents, the candidate should demonstrate empathy for why parents might sometimes be 'difficult'.)

Paragraph Five:
I gained work experience at Frimley Park Hospital where I shadowed a consultant ***orthopaedic*** surgeon and a ***junior*** doctor. I had the opportunity to witness surgical procedures such as a ***dynamic hip screw*** and the reduction of a displaced

radius fracture. I was also able to observe care delivered outside theatre in the form of ***ward rounds, fracture clinics*** and morning trauma briefings. During time spent with a junior doctor I cultivated an understanding of the NHS medical ***training system*** and the workings of a multidisciplinary team. Furthermore I accumulated a realistic appreciation of the challenges associated with a medical career. My experience demonstrated to me the necessary motivation and commitment required to withstand such trials.

- Tell me about the role of an orthopaedic surgeon.
- Tell me about the role of a junior doctor.
- I am a patient; describe a dynamic hip screw operation to me.
- Tell me about ward rounds and fracture clinics.
- Tell me about the medical training system.
- Orthopaedic surgeons sometimes have a reputation for being unkind. Have you found this to be true? (As with the question above regarding difficult parents, some empathy is required here for surgeons' workloads. Also, certain character traits are needed in good surgeons, who have to be able to operate calmly in trauma situations in the middle of the night. Like many strong character traits, there are pros and cons.)

> Go through your personal statement carefully and pick out areas which could be questioned in your interview. Be careful to think broadly about the areas you mention.
> If you have mentioned operations, procedures or diagnoses in your statement, ensure that you not only understand them, but have read around the subject and most importantly, have thought about patients.

Ethics

Most schools will ask a question which relates to ethics, often in the form of a clinical scenario. There are a few general things to consider. Firstly, these questions are as much a test of your attitudes as they are your knowledge. No knowledge will make you seem unmotivated and ill prepared. However, time and time again we see candidates answer ethics questions with utter certainty, based on a modicum of knowledge. Ethical dilemmas, by definition, usually do not have a 'right' answer, and it is not advantageous to be certain of a right answer. Far better to give both sides of the argument. However, it is completely acceptable, and sometimes necessary, to give your opinion, taking all arguments into account.

There are a few ethical principles and facts which would be worth knowing as they are often referred to at interview:

- Basic ethical principles underlying medicine
  - Non-maleficence
  - Beneficence
  - Autonomy
  - Justice
  - Futility
- Good Medical Practice (discussed earlier in this book)
- Capacity and consent

  - Including Gillick/Fraser competence
- Confidentiality
  - And breach of confidentiality
- End of life
  - Palliative care
  - Assisted suicide

Basic ethical principles underlying medicine

Doctors make ethical decisions as part of their daily work. Some decisions are more complex than others, but there are a few guiding principles to help with this decision-making. Non-maleficence, beneficence, autonomy, justice and futility are the foundations on which all decisions are based.

Non-maleficence

This is the most important of the principles, sometimes given as *'first, do no harm'*. This means that no act by a doctor should be prompted by a desire to cause pain or damage to their patient. At its extreme, this includes deliberately killing a patient for whatever motivation. Alternatively, many treatments do make the patient feel worse before their health improves. People with cancer, for example, often feel comparatively well in spite of the seriousness of the disease. Chemotherapy and radiotherapy have severe side effects, significantly reducing the quality of a patient's life before it improves again. This leads to the concept of:

Beneficence

Doctors must act in the best interests of their patient. Sometimes these 'best interests' involve causing short term reduction in quality of life but the ultimate aim must be to benefit the patient. Best interests are dependent on the individual, their beliefs and not necessarily those of the doctor (or the relatives). This relates to the concept of:

Autonomy

Patients have autonomy – as a generalisation patients must give consent to all treatments, investigations etc. and have the right to refuse any or all of these if they wish. However, no one has the right to demand treatment or a medical procedure. Issues surrounding lack of consent are detailed below.

Justice

Patients must be treated 'justly'. Treatment decisions should be based on clinical need and not on personal opinions, prejudices or the doctor's own cultural background. For example, an alcoholic with liver-capsule pain is just as entitled to analgesia as a child who has tripped and broken their wrist in the school playground.

Futility

A doctor cannot justify offering a treatment or procedure which is almost certainly futile. All treatments and procedures have associated risks, if there is no potential benefit, then by definition, risks will outweigh benefit and the principle of non-maleficence is violated without the counterbalance of beneficence.

MMI example of an ethical dilemma

A recent court case in the UK considered a request from a family for medical support and management to be withdrawn from an individual who is in a near-vegetative state. Some family members and staff believe that the patient is expressing emotions and has some small voluntary movements, others are certain that these are just reflex reactions and that the patient is unaware of their surroundings. If you are the lead doctor for this patient, consider the ethical implications of continuing treatment or withdrawing treatment.

In answering this question well, you will need a basic understanding of ethical principles, an ability to see both sides of the argument, and a structured approach to your answer.

You might start with something like:
"This is a very sad situation and whilst this extreme scenario may not happen on a day to day basis, disagreements between doctors and relatives, particularly when a terminally ill patient lacks capacity, must be relatively common."

This type of introduction shows that you have some empathy, compassion, and recognise the relevance of the question.

You would then need to give your answer some 'content'.
You could structure it in terms of ethical principles:

"In terms of non-maleficence, it is arguably harmful to keep the patient alive (in some ways it is awful to think that such a patient might have any awareness of the situation). However,

death cannot really be thought of as good, and so we must consider beneficence.

"In terms of beneficence, there are two sides to the argument of what is in the patient's best interests; either no death, or a good death. On the one hand...."

When you have added 'content' to your answer, you will need to conclude. This might take the form of an opinion, or it might be some additional information, for instance,

"Whilst any good doctor should be compassionate and empathic towards the relatives, it is ultimately the doctors decision as to what best interests are. However, where there is dispute and uncertainty, such doctors should seek help from their colleagues, defence union and ultimately the legal system."

Capacity and consent

Reproduced with kind permission from the Medical Protection Society:

Competence and capacity

Patients need to be competent (have capacity) in order to give their consent. Everyone over the age of 16 is assumed to be competent.

The Mental Capacity Act (MCA) 2005 (for England and Wales) states that a person cannot make a decision for themselves if they are unable to:

- Understand the information relevant to the decision
- Retain that information

- Use or weigh that information as part of the process of making the decision
- Communicate their decision (whether by talking, using sign language or any other means).

Normally competent individuals may lose capacity temporarily because of pain, shock, drugs or their condition. Patients who have mental health problems may have difficulty making decisions about their treatment, but this should not be assumed. There may well be a difference between obtaining consent to treat them for their mental health problem and another health problem that they encounter.

On each occasion that treatment is required for a patient who does not have the capacity to consent, a decision is made in the best interests of the patient. The MCA states the following should be considered:

- The past and present wishes of the patient (especially any written statement when the patient had capacity)
- Religious beliefs or values expressed by the patient when competent
- The views of relevant others (eg, carers, relatives)
- The patient should be involved in the consent process and, where appropriate, encouraged to give their consent to particular aspects for which they do have capacity.

Assessing capacity can be very difficult where patients suffer from serious communication problems.

Frame questions in such a way that the patient will need to give a full response in order to assess their understanding, eg, "Tell me what you understand by..." rather than "Do you understand?" which may only require a yes or no answer.

How do you assess capacity?

The assessment of capacity is decision-specific and there are two stages:

- Is there an impairment of or disturbance in the functioning of the patient's mind or brain? If so,
- Has it made the person unable to make this particular decision?

The MCA includes a checklist of factors to be considered and makes reference to a lasting power of attorney (LPA). A competent adult can nominate an LPA who may be able to make decisions about the continuation or withdrawal of life-sustaining treatment. This agreement must expressly indicate the power to make decisions about personal welfare (which may or may not include life-sustaining treatment).

The nominated LPA starts to make decisions on behalf of a patient when they lose capacity, and it is up to a medical professional to decide when this is.

Refusing consent

You should listen to patients and respect their views about their health, even if you do not agree with them.

Patients can refuse consent. If they are competent, they are entitled to refuse consent, no matter how illogical this seems. If this happens, it is a good idea to explain to them the possible consequences of their decision, not necessarily with a view to changing their mind, but to clarify the situation.

The MCA requires that all factors, including religious beliefs or values expressed by the patient when competent, be taken into consideration.

Patients can withdraw consent during a procedure – but if stopping the procedure at that point would genuinely put the life of the patient at risk, the practitioner may be entitled to continue until this risk no longer applies.

Elderly patients

As patients get older, there is a temptation to believe that they have decreased capacity to take decisions about their treatment. However, [doctors] should always work on the assumption that capacity to give consent for treatment exists, unless it is proven otherwise.

The Department of Health's guidance on *Seeking Consent: Working with Older People* points out that: "It should never be assumed that people are not able to make their own decisions, simply because of their age or frailty."

End of life decisions

Before people lose the capacity to consent to treatment, particularly as a result of a progressive condition, they may make an advance decision or directive (or living will). If the statement was made by a competent adult, and there is no reason to believe that they have changed their mind, it should be respected.

The MCA provides some protection for doctors dealing with advance decisions. In particular, it provides a safeguard for doctors acting on advance decisions.

Doctors will not be held liable if they:

- Are in doubt over whether there is an advance decision and therefore provide treatment

- Believe a valid and applicable advance decision exists and withhold or withdraw treatment.

Where there is doubt, the courts will decide whether an advance decision exists and whether it is valid and applicable to treatment. Until the court decides, nothing should prevent the provision of life-sustaining treatment or anything believed to be necessary to prevent a serious deterioration in the patient's condition.

Children and young people

Anyone aged 18 and over is assumed to be a competent adult who can give their consent. In Scotland, the legal age of capacity is 16.

Aged 16-17

Young people of this age are treated as if they were adults. They are assumed to be competent. However, if they refuse a treatment, this can be overridden either by someone with parental responsibility or the courts.

Under 16

Children under 16 are also often competent. *Gillick v West Norfolk and Wisbech Area Health Authority* (1985) found that a parent's right to consent to treatment on behalf of a child ends when the child has sufficient intelligence and understanding to consent to the treatment themselves (when the child becomes "Gillick competent").

It is for the doctor to decide whether a child has reached this level of maturity and understanding. One challenge,

particularly in a large practice, is to apply the guidelines consistently.
Continuing education is important to make sure that all healthcare professionals understand Gillick competence and how to apply it. Unless the patient objects, you should also involve parents or others with parental responsibility, particularly in more serious situations.
If children under 16 refuse a treatment, this can be overridden by someone with parental responsibility or the courts. However, when there is a difference of opinion between the young person and their parents, this is usually resolved within the family. If there is no need for an immediate decision, it is clearly preferable to delay a decision until this can be resolved.

Example MMI questions

If a patient is unconscious and an operation is needed urgently, is consent needed and from whom?

In this case, the principle of beneficence allows the doctor to act in the patient's best interests without consent from anyone. However, only life-saving treatment can be given. If the surgeon happens to notice an in-growing toe-nail whilst pinning fractures in the long-bones of a trauma victim, pinning the fractures is a life-saving procedure which does not require consent. Removing the in-growing toe-nail without consent could be perceived legally as battery but more importantly in this context is unethical because it is not life-threatening; treatment can wait until the patient is in a position to give consent. Consent/refusal from another is only binding if that individual has LPA, although one would always try to take relatives feelings into consideration.

Discuss situations from your work experience where treatment has been given without consent.

Was the consent merely implied, or was the treatment 'in the patient's best interests'. Examples might include:

- Cleaning a soiled patient with dementia who does not answer you. (?Best interests; soiled areas can become sore and infected; the assumption being made is that the dementia renders the patient incompetent, but dementia does not necessarily mean this.)
- Restraining a life-threateningly injured patient because they want to find their child. (?Best interests; they need emergency treatment; one is assuming here that pain and emotional anguish is causing the patient to temporarily lose capacity but again, this might not necessarily be true.)
- Giving a heart attack patient some medication without first explaining what it is. (?Implied consent of being in A&E connected to monitoring equipment and being accepting of help.)
- Taking blood without fully explaining what it is for. (?Implied consent of volunteering ones arm and having a tourniquet put around it.)

Do you think it is reasonable to take a patient with mild dementia to the nursing home's dining room when she is saying she is not hungry?

This question tests your awareness of the principle of autonomy and right to refuse treatment. However, the question also tests you realism and empathy:

"A fundamental principle of our medical practice is that we must seek consent and should only treat without someone's consent if they are both unable to consent and that the treatment is in the patient's best interests. There are a number of issues here surrounding what the treatment is, and whether she is refusing it. There is also the question of whether she has capacity. Finally, it is worth considering why the patient is not hungry. (Intro.)

"Firstly, there are two aspects to 'treatment'; taking a patient to the dining room is just that, and does not mean insisting that she eat. However, her objection that she is not hungry in response to being taken to the dining room does seem to imply that she is refusing to go to the dining room. During my work experience, I have seen many situations like this where there has been a degree of negotiation, with staff suggesting that the patient have 'just a little bit', or that one of their fellow residents would like to see them. (Analysis of the question and evidence, including work experience.)

"If she were to refuse more obviously, for instance 'do not take me to the dining room' then this is refusal. But I wonder if she lacks capacity. It is impossible to say from the information given whether she lacks capacity, but the suggestion that she has only mild dementia does imply that she has capacity. Capacity relates to the treatment as well as the ability of the patient, and even patients with severe dementia may well be able to decide which room they would like to be in, even if they cannot consent to more complex things. (Knowledge of capacity, in the context of the question.)

"As with so much in medicine, there is never a never or an always! This is a typical situation in nursing homes. Staff numbers are often limited and whilst refusal to go to the dining room should be honoured, does this put other patients at risk if staff are looking after a patient who is not in the dining room? Or will the family complain if this lady loses weight? Or will she be hungry in an hour? (Empathy for nursing home staff and realism into the grey areas within medicine.)

"Finally, we must always care for the patient in the broadest of terms. What is the reason for her lack of hunger? We need to consider her dementia, as well as other illnesses, such as a simple infection, or something very sinister. Perhaps she is depressed. Or maybe the food is awful or being served at odd times. It is worth trying to manage things in a shared way, where the patient is part of the team making decisions about her care." (Analysis of why the patient might be hungry, demonstrating analytical skills. The final sentence is a wonderful conclusion which circles back to the principle of autonomy.)

This answer is good because it contains:

- Structure
- Knowledge (ethics)
- Knowledge (work experience)
- Empathy and realism

Confidentiality

Confidential information has connotations of being 'secret' and private with regard to those involved. On disclosing a piece of confidential information, you are trusting someone with something personal. A medical example of this would be if a patient were to visit their GP about experiencing panic attacks; sharing the information would be done under the presumption that it would remain between themselves and the GP. When it is necessary that information is passed between health care professionals, this is done on a 'need-to-know' basis, i.e. no more information than absolutely necessary is disclosed. A method implemented in the NHS to ensure confidentiality (predominantly regarding data) is the 'Caldicott guardian'. This is a person working within the health care organisation acting as the 'conscience' of the organisation (Department of Health, 2010); they must ensure that patient information is adequately assessed before anything can be shared with third parties.

Is adhering to confidentiality realistic in all situations?

There are three main situations in which the GMC acknowledges the need to break confidentiality. When:

(a) it is required by law

(b) the patient consents – either implicitly or for the sake of their own care

(c) it is justified in the public interest

Sometimes there is a legal duty to disclose. Upon arrival of a gunshot victim in hospital, the police should be informed immediately to assess the risk to the public. In terms of consent, if a patient is too ill to work they may require proof from a medical professional, which they then share with external agencies. Finally, perhaps the most ambiguous and difficult to assess point is the last, weighing up the interest of

the patient in relation to that of the public. This is extremely important in the case of notifiable diseases (Public Health Act, 1984), a set of highly infectious or damaging diseases that are deemed to be 'unethical' if allowed to spread e.g. measles. Thus the doctor must inform the authorities in the event that they diagnose a notifiable disease. Other situations where confidentiality can be breached in the interests of public safety would include issues of child abuse (or abuse of any vulnerable person), or serious mental illness where either the individual or others are at risk.

A public situation where the ethics of confidentiality were in dispute was the case of the Labour politician Mo Mowlam, who was Secretary of State for Northern Ireland. She was diagnosed with a malignant tumour of the frontal lobe. Not only did she have a short life expectancy (approximately 3 years), but the position of the tumour meant that it could impact her decision making and impulsivity. With a job affecting the general public, her condition could potentially have influenced her political motives and decisions. Mowlam decided to remain quiet, leaving Mark Glacer (her oncologist) in a difficult position, which he described it as a 'professional nightmare'. He maintained her confidentiality.

Example MMI question

Your married patient is diagnosed with HIV. He tells you that he has no plans to tell his wife. What should you do?

Although there are laws governing situations when confidentiality must be kept or broken, this situation is far from black and white and is often debated by clinicians and ethicists. When does a patient cross the line from being safe to being a danger to themselves and/ or others? How can a clinician decide whether the overall benefit to the family and community may outweigh that of the patient? With whom does the clinician's interest lie and where should the line be drawn? These are all difficult questions which weigh heavily on the doctor who has to make critical decisions.

This is a good question to practice with a friend. See if they can mark you against the following criteria:

- Structure to the answer (Intro, content, conclusion)
- Understanding of HIV as a serious infectious disease
- Understanding of the principle of confidentiality
- Understanding that confidentiality can be breached when there is a serious risk to the public
- Development of the two sides of the dilemma (to breach or not to breach). Ideas might include that we do not know if the couple have a sexual relationship, we do not know if patient has sex with other people and we do not know if someone he has sex with will necessarily contract the disease (especially if he uses a condom). Finally, HIV is not a notifiable disease, which in itself is interesting.
- Recognising the importance of confidentiality; without it the doctor-patient relationship would be lost.

End of life

This is a hugely important topic for doctors, candidates, patients, relatives, the nation and the NHS. There is often something in the news regarding assisted suicide and the right to die, or care in nursing homes, or NHS funding for our ageing population, or the use of end of life care pathways (i.e. the Liverpool Care Pathway). As end of life is so important (indeed, it happens to us all), you should have a good understanding of end of life issues. You should also have a real empathy and sympathy for those on the receiving end of the care we give.

The topic of end of life care lends itself extremely well to the sort of discussion one expects from an MMI station.
Below are three subject areas which could easily form the basis of an MMI station. Firstly, an insight into the views of relatives. Secondly, an understanding of palliative care. Finally, a summary of the current law relating to assisted suicide.

A good death – a relative's perspective

The morning my Mum left her home to go into the local hospice for respite care she picked up her treasured photograph of the entire family who were so dear to her ; husband, three children and eight grandchildren and kissed it goodbye. Watching her I suggested that she pack it and put it on her bedside table in the ward.

"No need for that, I'll be home soon!" she said too brightly. She didn't believe the words she spoke, and neither did I but we would never have admitted it.

My Mum had breast cancer that had spread to her brain, liver and lungs and she was getting more feeble by the day. Fiercely independent she wouldn't accept help from her family and finally it was her GP who persuaded her that a stay in a hospice would be of benefit.

She wasn't always open to good advice, my Mum. We smile now at the memory that she chucked out a very lovely visiting MacMillan Nurse who enquired, among other things, about her finances. Trying to be helpful she informed Mum that there was an end of life state benefit that she could claim. "I've never spent a penny in my life that I didn't earn and I'm not starting now!" was my Mum's angry reply. She seized back the cup of tea she had made for the surprised Nurse and put her out onto the front step, closing the door behind her.

The Hospice soothed Mum and found a way to make it seem like she was helping herself, when actually it was them who helped her. A lot. Staff chatted to her, clinicians and non-clinicians alike, and most importantly they listened. They made sure she never missed Countdown, her favourite afternoon TV programme. They washed and set her hair, they asked how she liked her porridge in the mornings and how crispy she preferred her bacon. They even set her up with cushions on a bench in the garden so she could have a smoke when she felt the urge. Mum liked, trusted and appreciated the staff for all their efforts and was therefore relaxed instead of fearful when they increased or decreased a drug dosage, or swapped one medication for another.

In the Hospice, she did still feel like a patient. She wasn't daft and was well aware that she wasn't at home in her own bed. But the calm atmosphere, the high staff to patient ratio, the personal attention and emphasis on her dignity at all times made her feel like a very important patient. She was confident in the care she was receiving which freed me and the rest of her family to concentrate on just being with her during her final days.

We didn't feel the need to ask questions, challenge or chivvy decisions or complain about the way Mum was being cared for or how long she had to wait for services and treatments. In the smaller home from home setting of the Hospice everything ran smoothly and to time.

The high standard of Hospice care was liberating for us all. We had time to talk, to keep quiet company, to stay overnight and most importantly to be with her in a peaceful setting when she died - just a week after she had been admitted.

We also faced the imminent prospect of her death by the awareness that other patients died during her stay and made a collective peace with the fact. The Hospice formed an alternative universe around us. Of course none of us wanted to be there – we wanted Mum to be restored to full health. But that wasn't possible, so we all slowly came to terms with that, and in an NHS setting it was certainly the best place to be. I cannot put into words the gratitude we feel for the staff who fulfilled so well the ethos of the hospice that every patient is special. They took care of us too. Both my sister and I had grief counselling there in the months that followed our Mother's death.

When you lose a loved one there is no escaping the pain of loss, but our Hospice experience made us grateful for how she died and how the feelings of the whole family were fully considered. It made all the difference. So much so that now, a decade later, I volunteer at the Hospice because I want to give back for all the care and attention they gave my family when we most needed it.

Many relatives do not feel this sense of gratitude. Many feel betrayed and angered by the care their loved ones received. These are, of course, the stories which make the news. There are many aspects to death, and where, when and how is not always what people hoped for. Of course, we will never be 'happy' with death, but we should try to make it as acceptable as possible.

Palliative care – experience of a junior doctor

My worst experience of the last few years was being in the Emergency Department (ED) when two patients were admitted within ten minutes of each other. Both were acutely unwell, and it rapidly became clear that both were in their final hours of chronic disease and that intervention would be futile. The resuscitation area of an ED is not a good place to die - it is noisy, crowded and there is no privacy for either the patients or their families. One of these patients, it later transpired, had wished to die at home and the other in the local hospice.

Recently there have been a number of initiatives to try to improve the quality of death for patients and to broaden access to palliative care. Palliative care has traditionally focussed on cancer patients because of cancer's relatively predictable disease trajectory. For other disease states, progression can be far more difficult to predict and hence so is the transition from palliative to terminal care, i.e. the point where managing the patient's symptoms to improve their quality of life becomes managing their symptoms to improve the quality of their death.

However, things are changing and patients often survive cancer long-term. For example breast cancer patients can be under the care of the palliative care team for many years, and many develop a disease progression far more akin to other chronic diseases, where there are repeated episodes of worsening and then partial recovery rather than a steady trend of worsening health. Additionally, if it is assumed that the average GP has twenty patient deaths per year, only five of these are likely to be from cancer, a few will be sudden, unexpected deaths, and others will be from chronic diseases which are not cancerous in origin.

'Palliative' comes from the Latin, *palliare*, 'to cloak'. The role of the palliative care team is to help to manage symptoms for patients for whom active treatment is no longer possible or appropriate. Not all people who are dying will need the care of a palliative care team; if their own specialist team can manage their symptoms for them, then the palliative care team are not required. The palliative team is a multidisciplinary team comprising the patient themselves, the patient's family and/or carers, specialist doctors, nurses, pharmacist, physiotherapist, occupational therapist, dietician, social worker, chaplain (with access to spiritual advisors from a range of religious backgrounds and whose services are as much for staff as patient) as well as the patient's GP and hospital doctors who specialise in the disease from which the patient is dying. The patient's own GP and community care staff have an increasingly large role in palliative care.

Ideally, facilities on offer will include in-hospital specialists, outpatient clinics run by specialists, day-hospice, a drop-in centre with staff available to provide advice and support when needed, specialist community nurses and a hospice. Furthermore, there should be help and support for the families and projects for children, for example, 'Jeremiah's Journey' to help children to come to terms with the death of a close relative. The hospice is not usually only for end of life care; much of their work will involve admitting patients for assessment and control of symptoms before discharging the patient home to carry on with the best possible quality of life for a little longer.

If you ask patients early on in their disease where they want to die, they usually say that they want to die at home with their family round them. Later in the disease course, as symptoms become more difficult to control and they have used the hospice facilities, many change their minds and their preferred place of death becomes the hospice – they feel safe there, know the staff, and know that their symptoms will be controlled properly. They also know that there will be no attempt made to resuscitate them should they die in the hospice.

When a patient enters the terminal phase of their disease, usually with only hours to days left, healthcare professionals will often agree that the patient should be put on the Liverpool Care Pathway (LCP). This Pathway is carefully designed to give the patient and their families the best possible death. All active interventions are stopped except those which are solely to manage symptoms. Symptoms which are common in the dying are anticipated and the drugs prescribed so that there is no delay in providing relief. Although some of the drugs used may shorten life, their primary purpose is only to relieve symptoms, not to hasten death. The LCP can be used in almost any environment from the patient's own home to an Intensive Care Unit in a specialist hospital.

Death is not the failure of medicine to keep the patient alive, death is a natural progression. The interventionist nature of modern medicine means that more thought needs to go into a good death rather than fighting to stave death off even in the last hours and minutes of life. Guidelines, education for healthcare professionals and facilities are being put in place to help to improve both the quality of life and the quality of death for a patient with a life-shortening disease.

Focus must always remain on providing patients and their families with a good death. For some, the definition of a good death includes choosing when and how to die.

Assisted suicide

With continuing advances in medical science, it is now possible to sustain the life of an individual with progressive and debilitating disease for months, years and even decades. However, support is growing for an argument that says people should have the right to a dignified death at the time of their choosing should they wish it. The issue arises when the individual in question requires assistance to commit suicide, from a family member, friend or healthcare professional. Is this an act of selfless mercy or is it murder?

There are a number of European countries where assisted suicide is legal including The Netherlands, Luxemburg, Belgium and Switzerland. Switzerland is particularly well known for its liberal views on assisted suicide and is the location of the Dignitas clinic where people can choose to pay for an assisted death. In the UK, assisted suicide is currently illegal. The Suicide Act of 1961 states that 'Aiding and Abetting Suicide' is a crime and is punishable by up to fourteen years in prison. The defendant could also potentially be charged with 'Murder' and, if convicted, would face a mandatory life sentence (fifteen years). Until recently it was not clear as to which situations would lead to prosecution and cases relied heavily on limited judicial president.

In October 2008 the case of Multiple Sclerosis (MS) sufferer Debbie Purdy came into the media spotlight. Purdy, who was diagnosed with progressive MS in 1995, was concerned that she would suffer an undignified death at the end of a long illness and decided that, at some point, she would choose an assisted death at the Dignitas Clinic. Before committing to this, Purdy wanted to seek assurance from the courts that her husband would not be liable for prosecution for assisting her in travelling to Switzerland to die. Purdy lost the case in the High

Court but she appealed the decision and requested clarification of the law on assisted suicide.

As requested by Debbie Purdy, the Director of Public Prosecutions (DPP) clarified the law on assisted suicide in 2010. The key points that arose from this are as follows:

- The victim must take his or her life; if the suspect takes the life of the victim they will be liable for prosecution for murder or manslaughter
- The victim must reach a clear and voluntary decision to commit suicide
- The suspect must be wholly motivated by compassion and should not stand to make significant financial gain from the death of the victim.
- If the victim had a terminal illness or degenerative condition, this will no longer mitigate against prosecution.
- Prosecution will be favoured in cases where a suspect unknown to the victim assists or encourages the victim to commit suicide. This is particularly relevant to healthcare professionals.

These key points were followed in a number of cases during 2010. Kay Gilderdale was charged with the attempted murder of her daughter Lynn who had suffered with ME for 17 years and was unable to eat, drink, speak or walk. Gilderdale was cleared of this charge. The judge in the case stated that Mrs Gilderdale was “a loving mother who was clearly acting in the best interests of her daughter”. However, in a similar case, Francis Inglis was convicted of murdering her severely brain-damaged son, Thomas. The key difference in this case was that, due to Thomas' condition, he would not have been able to communicate his wishes to die. It was held that his mother initiated the process of death whereas Kay Gilderdale had assisted her daughter in a process that she had begun herself with a morphine overdose.

In June 2011 The Royal College of General Practitioners and Royal College of Nursing unveiled a new patient charter on End of Life Care. The charter is a pledge by doctors and nurses to support dying patients and provide them with the best care possible. It discusses encouraging patients to 'think ahead' to the choices they will make and assisting them in 'recording decisions' about their care so that their wishes may be followed.

The debate on assisted suicide was reignited by the BBC documentary 'Choosing to die', produced by writer Sir Terry Pratchett. The documentary shadowed a number of people as they travelled to the Dignitas Clinic in Switzerland to die and discussed the need to legalise assisted dying in the UK. Pratchett was recently diagnosed with Alzheimer's and has openly discussed his intentions to attend the Dignitas Clinic to die. Pratchett went on to part-fund a report by The Commission on Assisted Dying, chaired by former Lord Chancellor, Lord Falconer, and includes members with expertise in law, medicine, social care, mental health, palliative care, theology, disability and policing. After a year of investigation, the results of this report presented a strong case for the legalisation of assisted dying in the UK. The commission described the current laws on assisted dying in the UK as “inadequate and incoherent” and they presented a legal framework that would allow terminally ill people to seek assisted suicide. The framework was aimed at those patients with less than one year to live and put forward strict eligibility criteria for these patients to fulfill. This criteria includes the following:

- Two independent doctors are satisfied with the diagnosis.
- The person is fully aware of all the social and medical help available.
- The person is making their decision voluntarily and with no sense of being pressurised or feeling like a “burden” to others.
- The person is not acting under the influence of mental illness.
- The person is capable of taking the medication themselves, without any assistance from others.

Under the suggestion of the report, GPs would be the ones to receive requests and facilitate assisted dying. It will also be the responsibility of GPs to uphold the safeguarding regulations detailed above. They would be required to assess a patient’s request for an assisted death and try to establish whether it is a serious request or a cry for help that may require alternative support. This kind of counselling would be an enormous undertaking for GPs and, if these suggestions ended up in a government bill, it would need great consideration and discussion to decide if GPs are indeed the appropriate professionals for this task.

Dignity in Dying, the campaign group who commissioned the report were pleased with the findings. Terry Pratchett, however, has said that the report does not go far enough in helping those wanting to die in this country. The report is clear in who should be eligible for assisted suicide if it were to be legalised in the UK and unfortunately these eligibility criteria exclude many people. In particular, Terry Pratchett's personal situation would be unlikely to meet the criteria so even if the law was changed it is likely that people like him would still have to look abroad for an assisted death.

The difficulty that the courts face in governing such a highly ethical issue is that the law attempts to objectify situations that are, by their very nature, extremely subjective. The facts of each case are very different and must be considered individually. A conviction of murder carries a mandatory fifteen year sentence and the judge cannot use their discretion to give a low sentence as may be done in a case of Aiding and Abetting Suicide. It is unlikely that anyone would think that it was the 'right' thing to do to convict a loving mother of murder for helping to end their child's suffering. However, without legal boundaries, 'assisted suicide' is open to abuse and could potential lead to some serious problems in end-of-life care.

One undisputed finding from the 2011 report was that it was extremely important to ensure that end-of-life care was of a very high standard throughout the UK. The report stated, "The provision of high quality end-of-life care must be a priority for government, independent of the issue of assisted dying. It recommends that in parallel with any change in the law, the government should also take action to tackle inequalities in end-of-life care and ensure that good quality end-of-life care is available to every person approaching the end of their life." The commission makes it clear that the decision to opt for assisted dying should not be as a result of concerns over inadequate end-of-life care or inadequate access to that care. This is something about which all parties are in full agreement and whilst the Government have no current plans to reassess the law on assisted suicide, this is an achievable goal to focus on.

Having read the above articles, you may now be in a better position to answer the following sort of questions, which would make ideal MMI questions:

- *What is a good death?*
- *What is palliative care?*
- *What are your views on assisted suicide?*
- *How is assisted suicide different to withdrawing life support from a patient in a vegetative state?*
- *Many terminal patients are admitted to hospital to die, when most would prefer to remain at home. Why do you think this happens and what could be done about it? (This requires empathy with patients. It also requires empathy for the relatives, carers, paramedics and doctors who may feel compelled to send the patient to hospital in case definitive treatment can be provided)*

Suggested Reading

www.gmc-uk.org

www.bma.org.uk

www.the-mdu.com

www.medicalprotection.org/uk

www.liv.ac.uk/mcpcil/liverpool-care-pathway

www.goldstandardsframework.org.uk

Mock MMI

As stated in the introduction, MMI is a variation on a theme. The schools are looking for the same skills as they were last year, or the year before. The schools using MMI are not selecting differently skilled candidates to those who do not use MMI. All of the questions which can, or have, been asked in MMI could be, or were, asked in other types of interview.

Here is a 'ten station' MMI. Get a friend of family member to show you each question, give you a minute thinking time, and then a strict five minutes to answer. If you would like a recording of the timed buzzers to practice with, please email us at *mmi@drprep.com*

The question is followed by suggestions for your interviewer to consider assessing. These are purely for use as a guide and should not be used as check lists, but merely ideas which the candidate may wish to explore.

For each question, it is worth asking for feedback on your body language, tone, general attitude, as well as your structure and whether your answer actually made sense.
Consider recording yourself.

1) What makes a good doctor?

Content: e.g.

Communication

Knowledge

Empathy

Caring attitude

Non judgemental

Interest in people

Realisation of other health professionals roles

Teamwork

Recognition of stress in oneself and others

Ability to recognise limitations

Willingness to accept responsibility

Willingness to keep updated

Practical skills

Ability to learn and implement new ideas and skills

A good answer would explore a few of these concepts *in the context of work experience.*

2) How has medicine changed over the last 100 years?

Content: e.g.
Hygiene
Healthcare workers and roles
NHS
Family planning
Changes in attitudes e.g. psychiatry
Biotechnology – investigation and treatment
Patient knowledge and expectations
The internet
Non 'essential' treatments e.g. cosmetic surgery
Evidence based practice including clinical trials
Preventative medicine and vaccination

Candidates often fear that their lack of any formal study of the history of medicine renders them useless. This question is at much a test of a candidate's ability to think on the spot, as it is a test of their knowledge. Any candidate should be able to discuss this for five minutes.

The candidate could consider key times and think about what the world was like in WWI, WWII and when they were born, for instance. 100 years ago there was the smallpox vaccine, but no polio vaccine, and certainly no HPV vaccine. Patients could not self diagnose using the internet. They did not have the contraceptive pill, nor the NHS. There were X-rays, but no CT or MRI. There were outside toilets, asbestos and coal mining. And so on.

3) What makes a ward run well?

Content: e.g.
Sufficient people & sufficient communication between them: e.g. ward clerk, nurses, doctors, health care assistants, occupational therapists, porters, physiotherapist, phlebotomists, cleaners.

Clear management, hierarchy and appropriate training.

Resources: resuscitation equipment, computers, phones, general clinical equipment, nursing equipment, forms, laundry, sluice.

Space: around beds, nurses station, relatives room, bathrooms, showers, side rooms.

A good answer would explore a few of these concepts *in the context of work experience.*

4) Instruct the examiner to draw a picture of a household object (such that they will then be able to identify it).

Skills: e.g.
Clarity
Structure
Patience
Allows time
Tries alternate approaches/starts again
Checks understanding

This is a test of communication. The interviewer/actor would be primed not to help you, so your instructions would need to be specific. We've had lots of fun with this question and the key is to take time to really consider what is the easiest thing to describe. Clocks are very easy, whilst toothbrushes and kettles are not. Five minutes is a long time, so there is no need to panic or rush. If a question is going horribly wrong, admit that it's going horribly wrong and start again.

5) Your friend keeps letting you down as he/she is often too hungover to keep arrangements. He/she has cancelled at the last minute on the last three occasions that you have arranged to meet him/her. It has happened many times before and other people have commented too. Discuss this with him/her:

The opportunity for role play is well known as being almost synonymous with the term MMI. It's the type of station that has had everyone talking, fretting, and blogging. Schools are rightly keen to be fair and objective and they are used to employing actors to pretend to be patients. The actors are very good, and it's best to simply think of them in character they are portraying. In this scenario, the actor would probably be very defensive if criticised, but might be engage if the candidate is gentle. This task is inherently affected by the responses of the 'patient'. However, there are a few key points to consider.

Always change critical statements into questions. Think about the differences between:
I think you're drinking too much and
Do you think you're drinking too much?
You stood me up and
Were you aware that you had forgotten to meet me?
Other people have said you've let them down and
Do you think anyone else is worried about you?
Offer empathy and support, e.g. '*That sounds awful, how can I help*?'

6) What are difficult patients?

The best answers are likely to be those who identify at the outset that difficult can mean a range of things. Good answers include work experience as all candidates should have seen a difficult patient.

Patients can exhibit difficult behaviour be e.g. angry, violent, tearful, risky, immature, defiant, mentally unstable, interfering, untrusting, non concordant.

Patients can be criminals, sex offenders, benefit fraudsters etc.

Patients can have different needs, eg. blind, deaf, disabled.

Difficult can also mean technically difficult (e.g. rare or complex diseases) or difficult due to time constraints (e.g. complex history, or emergency treatment); an anaesthetist might refer to 'a difficult airway' or a surgeon 'a difficult resection' or a GP 'difficult to manage (co-morbidities)'.

Empathy is important. Difficult behaviour can be the result of e.g. fear, sickness, tiredness, uncertainty, poverty, bereavement, bad medical care, bad social care, inappropriate expectations, raised expectations.

Remember that doctors should relish challenges.

7) I am from overseas – please tell me about the NHS.

As with question two, candidates often feel that they need to be an expert to answer this question. Some candidates misinterpret this as 'Discuss only the recent changes in the NHS'. Neither of these things are true.

Always remember to consider your audience. This person is unlikely to know much about the NHS, but that does not mean they are not intelligent. You are to explain the NHS to someone from overseas, you are not explaining the NHS to a child, which would require a different sort of communication. In a role play, it is sensible to ask the person where they are from, what they want to know, etc. You may know a little about that person's own health care system and be able to compare where appropriate.

Two types of structure have worked very well:

To discuss how to access healthcare in the UK; primary, secondary, the use of the ambulance service, role of pharmacists and so on.

The other option is to discuss the ethos of the NHS, why and how it started, its structure. The recent changes and planned developments are relevant, but need to form part of the answer, not all of it.

8) Your best friend's massive church wedding starts in twenty minutes and you are chief bridesmaid/best man. The bride's three year old niece has just spilt a big bowl of tomato soup over your entire outfit. Tell the bride.

Breaking bad news is a skill required of doctors. There are some key things to consider:

You must actually state the problem. (The analogy in medicine is that if a patient has cancer, you have to say the word cancer otherwise they may not realise the full import of what you are saying). You must take responsibility where appropriate. It is your responsibility to keep your suit away from children and bowls of soup. Apologise, don't be defensive or blame others.

Silence is very important. An upset person can't take much in after they've heard bad news. Offer a tissue, wait for some eye contact or another cue that you can move on. Ask open questions rather than making statements.

Exert common sense and sensitivity. You can't go to the shop and get a new outfit in the time, so don't suggest it. Make sensible suggestions *'I can wear my evening outfit; I won't match but everyone will be looking at you'*. The actor may have been instructed to become angry, for instance. Handle it as you hope that a doctor would handle and angry patient; calmly. Most importantly, leave your emotions behind when you go to the next station.

9) The examiner is blind. Please describe what you look like to them.

Out of perhaps one hundred candidates we have only seen one ask the actor if they had always been blind. We instruct our actors to become frustrated if someone mentions colour e.g. 'I'm wearing a blue jumper', and to retort that they've never seen a colour in their life. However we have seen the station done well without this knowledge.

Remember that blind does not mean stupid. You do not need to say that your long hair is growing out of your head, it is sufficient to say that you have long hair. (Similarly, with a deaf person who can lip read, you do not need to over-simplify your language, you need to slow down a bit and articulate properly)

Good candidates think broadly and discuss lots of things; physique, clothes, jewellery, hair, size of nose etc.

A couple of good candidates have described things they don't have, e.g. tattoos, piercings.

Analogy works really well in this station e.g.
'I'm a bit broader than you' or *'I think I'm a little bit taller than you'* or *'I'm wearing a similar shirt to yours'*.

A gold star is awarded to a candidate who asks '*Would it help you to feel my face?*'

10) You are sure that one of your house mates, in the year below, has copied a piece of your work and submitted it as her own, knowing that the person who marked your work has now retired. What would you do?

High standards are expected from our medical profession. Ultimately, the care of patients is your primary concern.
It is not acceptable for medical students to cheat (at its extreme, that individual might then treat patients when they are ill equipped to do so). However, you can demonstrate empathy. You should speak to your housemate first and offer support if appropriate, but ultimately highlight the problem and encourage them to disclose to their tutor. In the event that this does not happen, you should speak to the tutor yourself. You may be wondering if this is necessary if the individual had made a one-off error of judgment, had suffered a recent loss, for instance, but it is not for you to police this. If there are good reasons for their lack of probity, then the student should receive support from the right people. Otherwise, appropriate disciplinary action will be taken.

In summary you must:
Recognise that this is a lack of integrity.
Recognise the duties of a doctor as set out by the GMC.
Demonstrate concerns for the individual.
Discuss with the individual.
Encourage him/her to confess and seek help.
Be willing to tell the medical school.

And Finally

We hope that this book will help you to secure a place at medical school. We wish you the best of luck in your studies and look forward to meeting some of you during your training. However, the sad fact is that most applicants will not secure a place. Whilst some candidates should not be awarded a place at medical school, many unsuccessful applicants have great potential and may well succeed on subsequent attempts. Some of the best medical students that we have encountered admitted to having applied more than once before receiving an offer.

Age not withstanding, you might consider treating your unsuccessful applications as a learning opportunity. You will have undertaken some, if not all, of the following: work experience, the completion of application forms, preparation for and completion of entrance exams and interviews. This experience is enormously valuable – try to remember how daunted and uninformed you were when you started this process.

Above all, learn from your mistakes. Could you have started work experience sooner? Could you have found more valuable work experience? Did you get the most out of that work experience? Were you able to think deeply about patients, the pros and cons of medicine, and about yourself? Did you prepare adequately for the exams? Did you practise all the sample papers? Did you practise writing timed essays? Did anyone feed back to you on the standard of those essays? Did you frequently verbalise your medical aspirations and gain feedback on whether your desire and insight was apparent?

Few candidates prepare as well as they could, including the successful ones. If you have been through the process once, you have an advantage over the candidate who is navigating their way for the first time. Of course, we hope that this book goes a long way to ensuring that candidates do not feel lost in their application year, or indeed as they embark upon their training and beyond.

We wish you all the best in the pursuit of your vocation.